PLANTS AND PLANT LORE IN ANCIENT GREECE

J.E. RAVEN

Crocus cartwrightianus. Hymettos, 9 November
1930; Tourkovouno, 21 November 1930; from
Alice Lindsell's Botanical Sketchbook, f. 14v.

John Raven, drawing by his daughter Anna Raven

PLANTS AND PLANT LORE
IN ANCIENT GREECE

J.E. RAVEN

Accompanying essays by
Alice Lindsell
William T. Stearn
Nicholas Jardine
Peter Warren

Edited by
Faith Raven
William. T. Stearn
Nicholas Jardine
Marina Frasca-Spada

Drawing by
Anna Raven

Photographs by
Faith Raven

Plant portraits by
Alice Lindsell

First published in 2000 by
LEOPARD'S HEAD PRESS LIMITED
1–5 Broad Street, Oxford, OX1 3AW

© Faith Raven 2000

Faith Raven has asserted her moral right to be identified as the author of this work

ISBN 0 904920 40 2

Typeset by Cambrian Typsetters
Frimley, Surrey
Printed in China

CONTENTS

J. E. RAVEN

Plants and Plant Lore in Ancient Greece
Edited by William T. Stearn

PREFACE

I make no excuse for presenting these papers.

In 1976 my husband, the classicist John Earle Raven (1914–1980), delivered the Gray Lectures in Cambridge, on plants and plant lore in ancient Greece. Hitherto they have been known to a circle limited to the readership of the Athenian periodical, *Annales Musei Goulandris*, which published a version of them, edited by William Stearn, in 1990. A notable theme of the lectures is the exposure of apparently authoritative but in fact dubious identifications of plants in ancient Greek literature. They are a reminder of an earlier piece of botanical detective work which John Raven carried out in the Hebrides in 1948. This exploit was also known to a limited circle until made public in 1999 by Karl Sabbagh in *A Rum Affair. How Botany's 'Piltdown Man' was Unmasked* (Allen Lane, The Penguin Press), when it aroused considerable interest.

John Raven's earlier exploit and his Gray Lectures bring to botany the same qualities: of detection and deduction, of questioning of received wisdom – and of humour.

The Gray Lectures are here supplemented by the text of an illustrated talk given by my husband to the Alpine Garden Society of Oxford in 1971, and by two papers by Alice Lindsell (1878–1948), a pioneer in classical botany. Comments on the work and its relevance to similar studies today are made by W. T. Stearn, retired Senior Principal Scientific Officer of the Department of Botany, British Museum (Natural History), Nicholas Jardine of the Department of the History and Philosophy of Science, Cambridge, and Peter Warren of the Department of Archaeology, Bristol.

Faith Raven

ix

ACKNOWLEDGEMENTS

I acknowledge deep gratitude to all named editors of and contributors to this volume, and for other assistance, to William Barnes, Anthony Bryer, Harry Buglass, Serafina Cuomo, Susan Fox, Phyllis Hetzel and Roy Stephens.

Some sections are reproduced by kind permission of the Oxford University Press, and of the Goulandris Natural History Museum (Kifissia, Greece).

Faith Raven

STOP PRESS: As this book goes to press, notice must be made to Ingrid Waern, ed. William T. Stearn, "Flora Sapphica", *Annales Musei Goulandris*, 10 (1999), 171–80, just published. This is an account of the plants found on Mytilene (Lesbos) mentioned by the poetess Sappho and discussed by the Swedish classical scholar Ingrid Waern (1919–1997), originally published in *Eranos* 70, (1972), 1–31 and referred to with admiration by John Raven on pp. 7 and 8.

LIST OF ILLUSTRATIONS

JOHN RAVEN AND ANCIENT GREEK BOTANY

NICHOLAS JARDINE

Reprinted from *John Raven by his Friends*, eds. J. Lipscomb and
R. W. David (Shepreth, 1981), pp. 88–90.

The J.H. Gray Lectures were established, surprisingly enough, by a gift from the funds of the Cambridge Rugby Union Football Club. Under the relevant University Ordinance the funds are available to the Faculty Board of Classics 'to meet the expense of lectures on subjects not adequately provided for by the University Education Fund'. John was invited to deliver the 1976 Gray Lectures, four rather than the customary three, and chose as his subject 'Plants and Plant Lore in Ancient Greece'. It was with the liveliest anticipation that I came to Mill Lane for the first of the lectures. For though I already knew John well in several of his many capacities, as a mildly reproachful Senior Tutor, as a source of inspiration in my thesis research on the theory of classification, as a gardener, and above all as a companion in plant-hunting, I had never heard him lecture. And that, I was assured by no less an authority than John himself, was an experience not to be missed.

As performances the lectures were indeed remarkable. In anyone else the intricate presentation with its ironies and digressions, its self-depreciations and wilful dogmatisms, all delivered in hypnotically resonant cadences, would surely have seemed affected. With John, for all the meticulous preparation, it was miraculously spontaneous, the perfect vehicle for his insights and enthusiasms.

The scope of the lectures was ambitious, nothing less than the development of botany in all its aspects, aesthetic, taxonomic, agricultural and pharmacological, from Homer to Dioscorides, with an aside on Minoan depiction of plants thrown in for good measure. Somehow, by astute selection from a daunting body of material, John succeeded not only in covering all this, but in showing in fascinating detail just what treasures there are to be unearthed if only one argues rigorously from the right combinations of botanical, philological and historical data. But in one respect to read through these lectures again, with the accompanying drafts and notes, is a sad business. An early note reveals that he had planned a book on 'the history of botany in ancient Greece, the identity of the eight hundred-odd plants mentioned in extant Greek literature, and the veracity or otherwise of statements made about those plants in ancient books'. The field is a vast one, and virtually untouched by competent scholarship. With the notable exception of Miss Alice Lindsell, to whose pioneering work on the botany and topography of Theocritus' Idylls John paid tribute, those who had preceded him in that field received short shrift in the lectures. It is a field requiring quite extraordinary qualifications: a detailed first-hand knowledge of the geography, ecology and taxonomy of the Greek flora; the most meticulous philological scholarship and mastery of an immense range of sources; and, above all, the ability to combine bold conjecture, close reasoning and an eye for significant detail to build up a case from fragmentary evidence, the skills of a detective. John had these qualifications, and the Gray Lectures give a taste of a masterpiece that might have been.

But it would be altogether misleading to represent those lectures merely as a sketch, however full of original insights and exemplary scholarship, of the history of Greek botany. The real fascination lay elsewhere. Throughout the lectures John succeeded in communicating a specific enthusiasm, an enthusiasm which gave life to all his interests, classical, philosophical and botanical, the enthusiasm of the hunt. Sometimes the quarry was a person. In the opening lecture the hapless Sir William Thiselton-Dyer, F.R.S., successor to Hooker in the directorate of Kew, and author of the diagnoses of plant names that enliven the standard Greek dictionary, Liddell and Scott, is hunted down. With unholy glee the superficiality of his scholarship and the absurdity of his diagnoses are gently but remorselessly exposed. In the second lecture there is a delightful and revealing excursus on the nature of field-botany. Here the quarries are the endemic Cretan tulips. On meagre and inaccurate data they too are tracked to their haunts, and their habitats and reproductive habits shown conclusively to be quite other than once supposed. And finest of all is The Case of Hylas and the Water-Nymphs. Where, in precisely which pool, did Hylas succumb to the amorous nymphs, in the version of Theocritus' Thirteenth Idyll? 'Elementary, my dear Watson', we are told; and with irrefutable logic applied to the slenderest of textual, topographical and botanical clues John guides us to the very pool, near the mouth of the Neanthes on the island of Cos. Sad though it is that the plan for a history of Greek botany never came to fruition, it is hard not to envy John the sheer delight he took, and communicated, in these preliminary forays.

BIOGRAPHICAL AND BIBLIOGRAPHICAL INTRODUCTION TO JOHN RAVEN'S LECTURES ON GREEK PLANTS

WILLIAM T. STEARN

Under the auspices of the Cambridge University Faculty Board of Classics, John Earle Raven (1914–1980), former Lecturer in Classics, gave in 1976 four special lectures, the J.H. Gray Lectures, on *Plants and plant lore in Ancient Greece*. His listeners much appreciated them but until now they have remained unpublished. Their theme had engaged John Raven's attention off and on for many years; he even used a sabbatical year in 1969 to work at the botanical identification of plants in Ancient Greek literature. Unfortunately these lectures are the only outcome of that. Had he lived longer and if his other interests had been fewer and less enticing, he might have achieved something more comprehensive, as was indeed his intent. It has nevertheless seemed worthwhile to present them here, although with minor changes and omissions necessary to convert a diffuse spoken discourse into a more concise readable form serving as an introduction to a vast field of classical and botanical scholarship.

John Raven was not only an erudite classical scholar, a university lecturer in classics and a genial college tutor; he was also an enthusiastic amateur botanist with an extensive and detailed knowledge of British plants in the wild, especially those of restricted distribution. He delighted also in growing uncommon plants, as his book, *A Botanist's Garden* (1971), makes evident. These varied interests all contributed to his 1976 lectures. They derived from his ancestry, upbringing and education. His father Charles Earle Raven (1885–1964), the biographer of William Turner, John Ray and other early English naturalists and from 1932 to 1950 Professor of Divinity in the University of Cambridge, was probably the most scholarly and many-sided naturalist in Britain with expert knowledge of entomology, ornithology, botany and the history of early natural history; he served the Botanical Society of the British Isles as president from 1951 to 1955 and in 1964 the Linnean Society of London awarded him the prestigious H.H. Bloomer Award. His mother Margaret Ermyntrude (née Buchanan Wollaston) belonged to the scientifically distinguished Wollaston family which gave eight Fellows to the Royal Society of London. John Raven was born in Cambridge and died there, having spent most of his life in the service of the University as a lecturer and tutor; he retired in 1974.

As a schoolboy at Marlborough College he came under the influence of a great classics teacher, George Montague Sargeaunt, author of *Classical Studies* (1929) and *The Classical Spirit* (1936); moreover his grandfather had drilled him well in Latin and his father imparted a lasting interest in natural history. From Marlborough a scholarship enabled him to enter Trinity College, Cambridge and after graduation he became a Research Fellow of the College, transferring in 1948 to King's College. His first book on classics was *Pythagoreans and Eleatics* (1948); then followed *The Presocratic Philosophers* (1957), with G.S. Kirk, and finally *Plato's Thought in the Making* (1965). These scholarly works reflected his professional interests as a classicist. His travels over Britain as an amateur botanist in search of plants and particularly of members of the difficult and predominantly montane genus *Hieracium* led to collaboration with Max Walters, then Curator of the Cambridge University Herbarium, in writing *Mountain Flowers* (1956) for the New Naturalist series. The enforced leisure of illness he used in describing the dicotyledonous plants of the richly stocked and, to some eyes, eccentric garden which he and his wife Faith had created at Docwra's Manor, Shepreth, about 10 miles from Cambridge, which they bought in 1954. The volume on this, *A Botanist's Garden*, appeared in 1971. It begins: 'I, John Raven, wrote this book; my wife Faith took almost all the colour photographs', which are both attractive and informative.

John Raven made his first acquaintance with Greek plants when as an undergraduate at Cambridge he spent time roaming on foot in Thessaly and Crete, whence he introduced *Tulipa bakeri*, then a little known species, into this country. He was not the first to find this endemic Cretan species which was introduced into cultivation in 1926 by George Percival Baker; there is a coloured illustration in *Curtis's Botanical Magazine* 163: t. 9607 (1940). However plants derived from his collecting are still in cultivation and stimulated his interest in Cretan tulips, to which he referred in his Lecture 2. He made a further acquaintance with Mediterranean vegetation when, as a Research Student of Trinity College, he spent time in 1938–1939 at the British School in Rome. Nevertheless he did not visit the Mediterranean region again until 1955. On one of his subsequent travels he visited Cos and amused himself by identifying to his satisfaction the pool there which had in the 3rd century B.C. inspired the poet Theocritus in his poem on Hylas and the nymphs, as mentioned in Lecture 3. In 1971 he and Faith visited Crete and gave special attention to its wild tulips.

When discussing in his third lecture Theocritus' precise references to plants Raven obviously assumed his Cambridge listeners, mostly classicists, to be more familiar with the story of Hylas and the nymphs than is usual for non-classicists. In the saga on the pre-Homeric voyage of the Argonauts to Colchis, the boy Hylas, son of slain king Theiodamas and now the beloved but ill-treated page of Hercules, was sent to get a pitcher of clean water for his master, from whom he wished to escape. The Argonauts were encamped by the sea-shore. Going inland Hylas found a pool in which, however, a nymph was bathing, a view of a nymph, especially a naked one, being usually an unlucky happening for a human being.

However, on account of his good looks, she befriended him, hid him from searching Hercules and made love with him. In Theocritus' idyll 13 the handsome golden-haired youth finds three nymphs bathing in a pool, 'the sleepless Nymphs, dread goddesses for country folks... Eagerly the boy reached down to dip his great pitcher in the fount, but they all clung to his hand, for love of the Argive lad had fluttered all their tender hearts, and headlong into the dark pool he fell... There in their laps the Nymphs sought to comfort the weeping lad with gentle words' (translation by A.S.F. Gow). Hercules searched for him in vain. Botanical evidence caused Raven to believe he had found on the island of Cos the very pool Theocritus had in mind when he wrote his idyll. The exceptionally fine form of lesser celandine noticed by Raven is evidently the robust Mediterranean *Ranunculus ficaria* var. *grandiflorus* figured in *Curtis's Botanical Magazine* 153: t. 9199 (1930).

Botany and gardening brought to Raven's attention the large number of modern botanical generic names ultimately derived from the plant lore of Ancient Greece and presumably led him to the works of Theophrastus and Dioscorides, both little regarded by literary classicists but long esteemed by botanical historians, the first for his influence on Cesalpino and others in the 16th century, the other for his long-lasting compilation on medicinal plants. Apparently, according to Nick Jardine's contribution to the memorial volume *John Raven by his Friends* (1981, and here pp. xv–xviii), he had at one time planned to write a book on 'the history of botany in Ancient Greece, the identity of the eight hundred-odd plants mentioned in extant Greek literature and the veracity or otherwise of statements about them in ancient books'. This he never achieved. Not only would such an ambitious task be a formidable one even if confined to primary sources, it would also have to embrace the study and assessment of the enormous secondary literature so scattered through archaeological, botanical and classical journals and memoirs and so embedded in irrelevant material as to be difficult to trace and easily overlooked but containing much of value. The bibliography below well illustrates its dispersed nature. It would need years of critical attention by a single-minded scholar versed in Ancient Greek, Latin, French, German and Italian and in

Mediterranean botany to produce such a book. John Raven possessed the ability and the scholarship, but ill health, his many other interests and his premature death at the age of 65 put it beyond his accomplishment.

He revealed a small part of what he might have done in the four J.H. Gray Lectures printed here. These lectures had to be on subjects not adequately provided for by the University Education Fund. They had been instituted in 1926 not by an academic body but as a gift from a group of rugby footballers, the Cambridge University Rugby Union Football Club. The Reverend Canon Joseph Henry Gray (1856–1932), a classical Scholar at Queens' College, Cambridge had been their President since 1895. Raven, who had retired from his university post in 1974, chose as the 1976 lecturer to talk about *Plants and plant lore in Ancient Greece*. According to Jardine, 'as performances the lectures were indeed remarkable. In anyone else the intricate presentation with its ironies and digressions, its self-depreciations and wilful dogmatisms, all delivered in hypnotically resonant cadences, would surely have seemed affected. With John, for all the meticulous preparation, it was miraculously spontaneous, the perfect vehicle for his insights and enthusiasms'. Although these lectures touched upon only a minute part of their extensive subject, they made his listeners aware at least of its intricacy. To quote Jardine again, 'throughout the lectures John succeeded in communicating a specific enthusiasm, an enthusiasm that gave life to all his interests, classical, philosophical and botanical, the enthusiasm of the hunt'.

The first lecture made evident 'with unholy glee' the unreliability of some identifications by Sir William Turner Thiselton-Dyer (1843–1928) of plants mentioned in classical Greek literature. As regards Thiselton-Dyer's identifications in Hort's translation of Theophrastus, Suzanne Amigue's opinion (1988) coincides with John Raven's: 'l'*Index of plants* publié à la fin du tome II a fourni au *Greek-English Lexicon* de Liddell-Scott-Jones tout un contingent de déterminations imprudentes ou manifestement erronées, auxquelles l'autorité

de ce dictionnaire garantit une longévité regrettable' (*Théophraste, Recherches sur les Plantes*, 1: 2: 1988). Admittedly, as Director of the Royal Botanic Gardens, Kew from 1885 to 1905, he ably administered that institution but he was as disliked by many on the Kew staff as he was by the botanists at the British Museum (Natural History) who feared coming under his arrogant and autocratic rule. Raven, obviously riled by the dogmatic nature of his scholarship, treated him harshly and not altogether fairly by ignoring his series of often convincing articles in the *Journal of Philology*. Raven's comments on Theophrastus are valuable but reveal no knowledge of many illuminating publications by the Swiss botanical scholar Gustav Senn (1875–1945) listed below; an excellent modern assessment of the botanical work and influence of Theophrastus will be found in Agnes Arber's *The Natural Philosophy of Plant Form* (1950) and in A.G. Morton's *History of Botanical Science* (1981). Again he was obviously unacquainted with Martin Möbius's important well-illustrated survey (1933) of the plants depicted in Minoan art and the book of 195 pages by Kurt Lembach on the plants of Theocritus (1970).

Interpretations rather different from Raven's can just as plausibly be made for the stylized representations of plants revealed by Marinatos's excavations at Thera. Thus the plant representation on a cup (Marinatos, *Thera* 5: pl. 62 c), which Raven regarded 'as a remarkably faithful picture of one of the three Cretan species of tulip, namely *Tulipa cretica*', has been identified by Oliver Rackham (1978) as *Gagea graeca* (*Lloydia graeca*); personally I regard its exact identification as impossible. Raven suggested that the other plant portrayed on the bowl was a 'two-headed specimen' of *Ranunculus asiaticus*; Rackham considers it an 'only slightly stylized sketch of the remarkable fruit of *Biscutella didyma* L.', with which I agree. *Lilium martagon*, with which Raven identified the red lilies, has broad whorled leaves that a Minoan artist would not have failed to indicate, whereas *L. chalcedonicum* has numerous short leaves on the stem just as portrayed; moreover, though often with 5 flowers, it may have up to 10. Seemingly acquainted with both *L. candidum* and *L. chalcedonicum,* Minoan artists used essentially the same shape for both but distinguished them by white and red flowers. These notes may serve to indicate the difficulties which attend the identification of the plants known to the Ancient Greeks.

Raven stated in Lecture 4 that Dioscorides' need to distinguish kinds within a genus resulted in two-word names virtually indistinguishable from Linnaean binomials. This is particularly true for the genus *Euphorbia,* Dioscorides' τιθύμαλος (Tithumalos), where his τιθύμαλος δενδρίτης (dendrites) corresponds to Linnaeus's *Euphorbia dendroides,* τ. ἡλιοσκόπιος (helioscopios) to *E. helioscopia,* τ. κυπαρίσσιος (kuparissios) to *E. cyparissias,* τ. παράλιος (paralios) to *E. paralias,* τ. μυρσινίτης (mursinites) to *E. myrsinites* and χαραχίας (charachias) to *E. characias.* Apparently, however, Raven did not realise that such binomial nomenclature goes back far beyond Dioscorides and Theophrastus, 'back to the kind of names used from time immemorial by peasants, woodmen, hunters and herb-gatherers in many lands' (Stearn, 1957). Its consistent use in modern biology is merely a special application of age-old world-wide method of distinguishing by two-word names the kinds within a group such as knives, forks, spoons, chairs etc. 'Names of this kind have come into existence long before the invention of writing because they arise from a common human need and a common human limitation. This need is that of simultaneously indicating both resemblance and difference. The limitation is that of ordinary human memory; it is easier to keep two words associated than three or four' (Stearn, 1959).

Folk-names for species rarely exceed three words. In groups of species enough alike to have a vernacular group-name – the prototype and sometimes, e.g. if Greek or Latin, the direct ancestor of the modern botanical generic name – the species are often distinguished by a single epithet attached to this, as in the Ancient Greek, Latin, German, English and Malayan plant names:

ἀδίαντον τό λευκον, ἀδίαντον τό μέλαν (used by Theophrastus), *anagallis mas* and *anagallis femina* (used by Pliny), *weiss Seeblumen* and *geel Seeblumen* (used by Fuchs), *wild mynte* and *water mynte* (used by Turner), *jambu ayer, jambu bol, jambu chili,* etc. (applied by Malays to different species of *Eugenia*), to cite but a few examples out of many from markedly different periods, languages and places. Binomial nomenclature began in the remote past of human speech since it is a convenient linguistic device expressive both of synthesis into groups and analysis into individual kinds, when such is wanted. The capacity and the need to perceive and indicate the common characteristics of many diverse objects from different regions have, however, only in recent times become strong enough to make it the universal name-method of biological sciences' (Stearn, 1957). Obviously when a species or indeed any object is distinct enough not to be confused with anything else, a one-word name formerly sufficed; some examples from Dioscorides' herbal are κάππαρις (kapparis), κυδωνία (kudonia), κισσός (kissos) and νήριον (nerion). An assessment of Dioscorides in Riddle's *Dioscorides on Pharmacy and Medicine* (1985), a book of 325 pages, supports Fairbairn's views quoted by Raven: 'While he may not have been the first to discover most of the usages, he industriously collected them from various lands, codified the data, and organized it in a clear, concise and rational fashion. For this reason he became the chief authority on pharmacy and one of the principal ones on medicine'.

Despite some comments above, these J.H. Gray lectures contain much worth being made available. Faith Raven put into my hands with a view to publication the literal transcript of her late husband's lectures as delivered. Inevitably these contained statements irrelevant to a printed version such as 'I should like to start this evening with a statement that I hardly think anyone among you is likely to dispute, namely that my last lecture did not err on the side of undue brevity', 'I immediately grant, of course, in case such a thought has already occurred to you', and 'Actually I will save you the trouble and, except for lengthening one unpronounceable abbreviation, read you exactly what you would find' and much else of a digressive conversational nature, together with Cantabrigian allusions of interest only to a Cantabrigian audience: these have been deleted. My aim in editing has been to retain all that seems relevant or interesting as a tribute to the scholarship of John Raven and to exclude merely that which would now detract from this. A copy of the full text is deposited in the library of the Department of Botany, British Museum (Natural History), London.

The main classical authors cited by Raven are, in chronological order, as follows:

Homer (before 700 B.C.)
Hesiod (c. 700 B.C.)
Sappho (c. 612 B.C.): cf. Waern, 1972
Aristotle (384–322 B.C.)
Theophrastus (c. 370–285 B.C.); cf. Amigues, 1988; Arber; 1950, Greene, 1909; Hort, 1961; Morton, 1981; Senn, 1928–1943; Stearn, 1977; Strömberg, 1937
Theocritus (c. 310–250 B.C.); cf. Gow, 1952; Lembach, 1970; Lindsell, 1937
Nicander (2nd cent., B.C.)
Crateuas (lst cent. B.C.); cf. Wellmann, 1897
Dioscorides (lst cent., B.C. or A.D.); cf. Arber, 1986; Berendes, 1902; Gerstinger, 1970; Greene, 1909; Killermann, 1956; Morton, 1981; Riddle, 1985; Singer, 1927; Stannard, 1966; Stearn, 1954; 1977; Wellmann, 1906–1912
Galen (129–c.199 A.D.)

Although Raven obviously consulted many works in the preparation of these lectures, their transcript lacks a bibliography. He specifically cited a few in the text and implied the existence of others since he hoped that his words would lead other people into further study of his theme: the following list may serve for their guidance. It includes references to recent works as well as earlier ones which he is unlikely to have known.

References

Amigues, S. 1988–1989. *Théophraste. Recherches sur les Plantes.* Vols 1, 2 Paris.

Andrews, A.C. 1949. Celery and parsley as foods in the Greco-Roman period. *Classical Philology* 44:91–99.

Andrews, A.C. 1956. Sage as a condiment in the Graeco-Roman era. *Economic Botany* 10:263–266.

Andrews, A.C. 1958a. The mints of the Greeks and Romans and their culinary uses. *Osiris* 13:127–149.

Andrews, A.C. 1958b. Thyme as a condiment in the Graeco-Roman era. *Osiris* 13:150–156.

Andrews, A.C. 1961. Marjoram as a spice in the classical era. *Classical Philology* 56:73–82.

Arber, A. 1950. *The Natural Philosophy of Plant Form.* Cambridge (Chapter 2, pp. 9–23 on Theophrastus).

Arber, A. 1986. *Herbals, their Origin and Evolution.* 3rd ed. Cambridge, etc.

Baumann, H. 1986. *Die griechische Pflanzenwelt in Mythos, Kunst und Literatur.* 2nd ed. Munich. English ed. *Greek Wild Flowers and Plant Lore in Ancient Greece*, translated and augmented by W.T. Stearn and E.R. Stearn (London 1993).

Berendes, J. 1902. *Des Pedanios Dioskurides aus Anazarbos Arzneimittellehre in fünf Buchern übersetzt und mit Erklärungen versehen.* Stuttgart.

Cameron, M. & Hood, S. 1967. *Catalogue of Plates in Sir Arthur Evans' Knossos Fresco Atlas,* London.

Diapoulis, C. 1980. Prehistoric plants of the islands of the Aegean Sea. In Doumas, C. (Ed.), *Thera and the Aegean World* 2:129–140. ·

Douskos, I. 1980. The crocuses of Santorini. *In* Doumas, C. (Ed.), *Thera and the Aegean World* 2:141–146.

Evans, A.J. 1921-35. *The Palace of Minos at Knossos.* 4 vols. London.

Gerstinger, H. 1970. *Dioscurides Codex Vindobonensis Med. Gr. I … Kommentarband zu der Facsimile-ausgabe.* Graz.

Gow, A.S. 1952. *Theocritus, with a Commentary and Translation*. 2nd ed. 2 vols. Cambridge.

Greene, E.L. 1909. *Landmarks of Botanical History. Part I (Smithsonian Misc. Coll.* No 1870). Washington, D.C. (Reissued 1983, edited by F.N. Egerton).

Hill, A.W. 1934. A botanist on the Holy Mountain. *Blackwood's Magazine* 236:81–86, 649–655.

Hort, A. 1916. *Theophrastus, Enquiry into Plants … With an English Translation*. 2 vols, London & New York.

Killermann, S. 1955. Die in den illuminierten Dioskurides-Handschrift dargestellten Pflanzen. *Denkschr. Regensburg. Bot. Gesellsch.* 24:3–64.

Lembach, K. 1970. *Die Pflanzen bei Theokrit*. Heidelberg.

Liddell, H.G. & Scott, R. 1940. *A Greek-English Lexicon*, New ed., revised by H.S. Jones. 2 vols. Oxford (sometimes cites as LSJ).

Lindsell, A.E. 1937. Was Theocritus a botanist? *Greece and Rome* 6:79–93.

Marinatos, S. 1968–1976. *Excavations at Thera.* Nos 1–7, Athens.

Moazzo, G.P. 1983–1986. Les plantes de Homère et de quelques autres poètes de l'antiquité. *Ann. Musei Goulandris* 6:95–109 (1983), 7:57–65 (1986).

Möbius, M. 1933. Pflanzenbilder aus minoischen Kunst in botanischer Betrachtung. *Jahrbuch des Deutschen Archäologischen Instituts* 48:1–39.

Morton, A.G. 1981. *History of Botanical Science.* London, New York, etc.

Negri, M. 1989. Theophrastus on geophytes. *Bot. Journ. Linnean Soc. London* 100:15–43.

Rackham, 0. 1978. The flora and vegetation of Thera and Crete before and after the great eruption. *In* Doumas, C. (Ed.), *Thera and the Aegean World* I: 755–764.

Randolph, C.B. 1905. The Mandragora of the Ancients in folk-lore and medicine. *Proc. Amer. Acad.* 40:487–537.

Riddle, J.M. 1985. *Dioscorides on Pharmacy and Medicine.* Austin, Texas.

Senn, G. 1928. Theophrasts Differentialdiagnosen für laubwerfende Eichen, Hist. Plant., II, 892–7. *Vierteljahrsschr. Naturf. Ges. Zürich*, Beibl. 15 (Festschr. H. Schinz): 509–541.

Senn, G. 1933a. *Die Entwicklung der biologischen Forschungsmethode in der Antike und ihre grundsätzliche Forderung durch Theophrast von Eresos* (Veröff. Schweiz. Ges. Gesch. Med. Naturw. 8). Aarau.

Senn, G. 1933b. Die Systematik der nordost-mediterranean *Pinus* Arten in Theophrasts Pflanzenkunde III. 9. 1–5. *Verh. Naturf. Ges.* Basel., 45:365–400.

Senn, G. 1934. *Die Pflanzenkunde des Theophrast von Eresos.* Basel.

Senn, G. 1941. Oak galls in the Historia Plantarum of Theophrastus. *Trans. R. Bot. Soc. Edinburgh* 60: 343–354.

Senn, G. 1943. Die Beschreibung der Tanne in Theophrasts Pflanzenkunde, Kap., 996–8. *Boissiera* 7:455–484.

Singer, C. 1927. The herbal in antiquity and its transmission to later ages. *Journal of Hellenic Studies* 47:1–52.

Stannard, J. 1966. Dioscurides and Renaissance materia medica. *Analecta Med.-hist.* I: 1–21.

Stannard, J. 1974. Squill in ancient and medieval materia medica. *Bull. New York Acad. Med.* 70:684–713.

Stearn, W.T. 1954. Codex Aniciae Julianae: the earliest illustrated herbal. *Graphis* 10:322–329.

Stearn, W.T. 1957. An introduction to the Species Plantarum and cognate botanical works of Carl Linnaeus. Introduction to Ray Society facsimile of Linnaeus, *Species Plantarum* vol. 1.

Stearn, W.T. 1959. The background of Linnaeus's contributions to the nomenclature and methods of systematic biology. *Systematic Zoology* 8:4–22.

Stearn, W.T. 1977. From Theophrastus and Dioscorides to Sibthorp and Smith. *Biol. Journ. Linnean Soc. London* 8:285–298.

Stearn, W.T. 1983. *Botanical Latin.* 3rd ed. Newton Abbot, etc.

Strömberg, R. 1937. *Theophrastea. Studien zur*

botanischen Begriffsbildung (*Göteborgs Kungl. Vet. - Samhälles Handl.* V. 6 no 4).

Thiselton-Dyer, W.T. 1914–15. On some ancient plant names. *Journal of Philology* 33:195–207 (1914); 34:78–96, 290–312 (1915).

Waern, I. 1972. Flora Sapphica. *Eranos, Acta Philologica Suecana* 70:1–11.

Warren, P. 1977. Did papyrus grow in the Aegean? *Arkhaiologika. Analekta ex Athenon/Athens Annals of Archaeology* 9:89–95.

Warren, P. 1978. The miniature fresco from the West House at Akrotiri and its Aegean setting. *Journal of Hellenic Studies* 99:115–129.

Wellmann, M. 1889. Sextius Niger. Eine Quellen-untersuchung zu Dioscorides. *Hermes* 24:520–569.

Wellmann, M. 1897. Krateuas. *Abhandl. Ges. Wiss. Göttingen, Phil.-Hist. Klasse*, N.S. 2: 1–32.

Wellmann, M. 1906–12. *Pedanii Dioscoridis Anazarbei de Materia medica Libri quinque.* 3 vols. Berlin.

PLANTS AND PLANT LORE IN ANCIENT GREECE

JOHN RAVEN

Edited by William T. Stearn

Reprinted from the *Annales Musei Goulandris*, 8 (1990), 129–180, by kind permission of the Goulandris Natural History Museum, Kifissia, Greece.

LECTURE 1

UNRELIABILITY OF SOME OF THISELTON-DYER'S
IDENTIFICATIONS OF GREEK PLANT NAMES

PLANTS OF HOMER

PLANTS OF SAPPHO

This disquisition on ancient botany begins with a philosophical diversion. When Chaerophon, the dog-like devotee of Socrates, asked the Delphic Oracle who was the wisest man alive, the Oracle replied, in what was probably the most creditable of all its recorded utterances, that it was none other than Socrates himself. Chaerophon was no doubt triumphant, but not so Socrates, who promptly set about the attempt to refute the Oracle by finding somebody who was demonstrably wiser than himself. The familiar story, immortalised in Plato's early Socratic dialogues, ends of course with Socrates eventually driven to the conclusion that it was his own knowledge of his own total ignorance that must constitute the exceptional wisdom attributed to him.

That short diversion has a perfectly serious moral in relation to dogmatic identifications of ancient plant-names. If, for example, you look up in the latest edition by H.S. Jones of Liddell and Scott's Greek-English *Lexicon* the possibly unfamiliar and certainly uncommon word αἰγίπυρος (aigipuros), you would find:ʹαἰγίπυρος, ὁ, rest-harrow, *Ononis antiquorum*, Theophrastus *H.P.* 2.8.3, Theocritus 4.25; αἰγίπυρον, τό IG 14.2508 (Nemausus)ʹ.

If next you look up the two crucial passages, the one in Theophrastus, the other in Theocritus, on which alone the identification with rest-harrow would seem to be based, what would you expect to find there? If not a full and detailed description of the plant, then surely at least a mention of some distinctive feature which points unmistakably not only to the botanical genus *Ononis* (itself incidentally an ancient Greek plant name), alias rest-harrow, but also to the particular species of that genus distinguished from all the many other species of *Ononis* by the appropriate specific epithet of *antiquorum*. But not a bit of it. In the Theophrastus passage the text is anyhow so dubious that it is by

no means certain that the word αἰγίπυρος should occur at all – and indeed in both Wimmer's and Hort's versions it does not; while even on the most favourable interpretation the only clause of the remotest relevance to the word's meaning, namely ὅποταν αἰγίπυρος ἦ πολύς, 'whenever there is plenty of αἰγίπυρος', throws precisely no light on the question. And even the passage from Theocritus is hardly more helpful. The mere line and a half – ὅπα καλά πάντα φύονται/ αἰγίπυρος καί κνύξα καί εὐώδης μελιτεία – add no more than the suggestion, itself implicit rather than explicit, that αἰγίπυρος may at least be regarded, as incidentally rest-harrow may not, as a typical ingredient of the lush flora of a river bank. For all his diligent scholarship Andrew Gow [1886–1978], in his edition of Theocritus, can do no better than quote from the *Anecdota Graeca* of Bekker the brief excerpt 'αἰγίπυρος πόα πύρρα ἦν αἶγες νέμονται' which looks like no more than a mere guess derived from the word's presumed derivation but can be fairly convincingly exposed as such by the obscure and obscene pun in the ancient explanatory note (scholium) on Aristophanes' *Frogs* to which Gow himself refers. Incidentally these last two almost useless passages provide the only evidence – and what evidence! – that any part of αἰγίπυρος is any shade of red. The ancient commentator (scholiast) on this particular passage makes matters little better by first describing αἰγίπυρος as ἀκανθῶδες φυτόν, 'a prickly plant', which some species of rest-harrow admittedly are, but then so are countless other Mediterranean plants, including, for instance *Eryngium maritimum*, sea holly: next telling us that it has 'a broad leaf like a lentil', which is decidedly more appropriate to sea holly than to rest-harrow; and finally pointing more tellingly in the same direction by applying to it the epithet γλαυκίζουσα (glaukizousa) 'bluish-grey'. Whence and why then the confident identification of αἰγίπυρος with rest-harrow rather than, say, with sea holly? The answer is in Henry Stuart Jones' Preface to the latest edition of Liddell and Scott's *Lexicon*; I need quote only the following brief excerpt:

Sir William Thiselton-Dyer, F.R.S., has for a long while been collecting materials for a Glossary of Greek plants and the publication of Max Wellmann's edition of Dioscorides, completed in 1914, has furnished a reliable critical text of the most important author in this branch of literature. Sir William Dyer has been most generous in placing the results of his study of Greek plant names at my disposal, and his identifications are not likely to be disputed.

Alas this last prediction, though it subtly contrives to convey a shadow of doubt, has so far proved only too true, with unfortunate consequences for so many reputable classical scholars.

Born in 1843, the elder son of a doctor practising in Westminster, William Thiselton-Dyer only begins to enter our purview when, in 1875, Sir Joseph Dalton Hooker, one of the great Directors of The Royal Botanic Gardens, Kew, got him appointed; he married Hooker's eldest daughter Harriet Ann and, after ten years as his assistant, in 1885 succeeded Hooker himself as Director and continued in that honoured and influential post until he eventually retired into a comparatively leisurely but still fairly full and active life divided between Oxford and Gloucestershire. He died in 1928. There can be little doubt that Thiselton-Dyer intended to publish a 'Glossary of Greek and Latin Plant Names' but, from his papers, this was still at the time of his death a very long way from completion. Those papers, comprising three notebooks and a number of manuscript articles and notes, were presented by his widow to the authorities at Kew.

There I have been generously permitted to peruse them at leisure. I could cite instance after instance of Greek plant names which Thiselton-Dyer somehow contrived to identify with modern botanical species on the basis (and this is the point) of what on a generous estimate can only be described as less than half the evidence available in extant Greek literature. One example must suffice, and for obvious reasons that shall again be αἰγίπυρος. In the last of his notebooks, which contains all his considered conclusions as incorporated by Jones in Liddell and Scott's *Lexicon* the entire entry under αἰγίπυρος runs as follows:

αἰγίπυρος Theocr. 4.25 [Theophr. f.l. H.P. 2.8.3] a spinous red-flowered plant, *Rest-harrow*. Ononis antiquorum.

That is all; though it clearly embodied more study and thought than is here explicitly indicated it still suggests to me too insubstantial a basis for an identification which has ever since been accepted as definitive. If you take my advice you will henceforth view every entry in Liddell and Scott (LSJ) under a Greek plant name with a measure of scepticism. Before starting on the outlines of a history of botany in ancient Greece, it was imperative first to indulge in a little such demolition.

The period to be surveyed, a few stages of it rather less skimpily than the rest, covers the better part of a millennium. It starts, like so much else, with Homer, and it ends with Dioscorides, the last Greek botanist with any claim to originality, whose celebrated herbal, the *De Materia Medica*, seems to have been published around 60 A.D.

Homer conveniently raises a number of points which will later become significant.

In the course of his various poems, the Hymns included, Homer mentions as many as 60 different plants. The overall total, however, is pretty meaningless unless you compare it with the totals both of later writers and of the actual flora of Greece, which is about 4300. More significant is, first, the proportions of the various types of classes of plants named (by which I do not mean anything as scientific as their botanical families or genera), and second the general uses to which these various types or classes are put.

Of this total of 60 slightly more than half, or, to be precise, 32, are either trees or shrubs. Though not infrequently trees are named for the use to which they are put, as, for instance, a ship is explicitly stated to be of oak or a hall of cedar wood, in the majority of passages in which they occur, and especially in certain recurrent Homeric similes, the purpose is of course purely literary or pictorial: to bring a dramatic scene more vividly before the reader's (or hearer's) eyes. The same is true also of a second group of plants, 15 in all, consisting in the main of the more striking wild flowers, the inclusion of which is almost always for the purpose of painting a more vivid picture. So, to quote the most obvious instance, Homer writes in the *Hymn to Demeter*, 1. 425: 'We were all playing in the lovely meadow and gathering in our hands the fairest flowers, the soft crocus and the iris and the hyacinth all mixed, and the roses' cups and the lilies, a wonder to behold, and the narcissus which, with the crocus, the broad earth had nourished'. Admittedly in a hymn to Demeter we might well expect that flowers would play a prominent part; but comparable passages occur in the Epics as well.

Such passages, if they tell little or nothing about botany, do at least serve to assure us, first, that from the earliest times the Greeks were not entirely blind to the colourful flowers with which every spring their countryside abounds, and second, that some at least of these flowers already had their popular and presumably standard names.

In addition to the two groups of trees and wild flowers, two smaller groups play a more vital part in the Homeric poems than the purely literary. First and most obvious are, of course, the crops. Of these, apart from the fruit trees, already included in my first group, there are nine kinds mentioned in Homer – four kinds of grain, four vegetables, and flax; he clearly knew some at least of the principles of agriculture. Even in prehistoric times several of the same staple crops were cultivated, and in much the same manner, as in Mediterranean countries to this day.

The last and smallest group of plants, for our present purposes perhaps the most important, comprises the four mentioned in Homer that were used for medicinal purposes. Of these four, only one – and that entirely impossible even for Sir William to identify – need detain us. Homer calls it simply 'bitter-root' and this is what he says about it (*Il.*, XI, 846):

There he laid him down and with a knife cut from his thigh the sharp, painful spear, and with warm water washed away the dark blood; and shredding in his hands the bitter root, the stiller of pain, he laid it on; and the wound dried up and the blood was staunched.

Thus even in Homer's day a rudimentary pharmacology was practised; note that it is the *root* of the plant, whatever the plant may be, that was already employed for medicinal purposes.

One or other of the three tendencies which Homer's elementary knowledge of botany already reveals – the aesthetic, the agricultural and the medicinal – inspires almost the whole of ancient botany from beginning to end. With the solitary exception of Theophrastus, every ancient author who ever touched upon plants did so for one of these three ulterior motives. Of all those whose botanical or quasi-botanical writings are still extant, Theophrastus alone, doubtless encouraged by Aristotle, regarded botany as an independent science of sufficient interest to stand on its own feet. Every other author I shall mention henceforth, however original and valuable may have been his contribution to botanical knowledge, approached the subject only as a means to some external end.

But, for all that, the botanical lectures and demonstrations that Theophrastus gave in the Lyceum and its garden do seem to have exercised an influence that extended far beyond the circle of his immediate pupils. As far as the poets are concerned at any rate, Theocritus reveals several of the qualities of a genuine field botanist, which can with fair confidence be attributed to the indirect influence of Theophrastus and must be accepted as in a strict sense epoch-making. Accordingly, I will now give some summary and highly selective observations on the attitude of a few pre-Theophrastan writers to plants and flowers. For various reasons, I shall take the fragments of Sappho as my text.

On pages 1–11 of *Eranos* 70 (1972) is an article entitled 'Flora Sapphica', by Ingrid Waern. Not only does that article for the most part reveal a combination of knowledge, caution and good sense by no means universal among scholars, not only does it most commendably challenge two or three of Thiselton-Dyer's plant identifications apparently accepted without question in LSJ; it has also the great additional advantages of first incorporating some needed statistics, and then of posing exactly the right questions. The most relevant of the authoress's general findings can be imparted in four relatively brief verbatim quotations:

1. Sappho's love of nature is incontestable. Hardly anywhere in Greek literature is it possible to find such a full and rich description of the characteristic features of the landscape as in Sappho's unfortunately too fragmentary poetry.

2. … the flora is the central object of Sappho's view of nature. The fauna of the island did not interest her in the same way. Only once does she mention a wild animal, fr. 58. 16 ἴσα νεβρίοισιν, in a simile. For the rest, she mentions only tame animals, birds and one insect. In her poetry there are goats and sheep and mules and horses. The four birds mentioned are all greatly beloved in poetry and mythology: they are Aphrodite's holy sparrows, the swallow, the nightingale and the halcyons. The same is applicable to the only insect she mentions, the bee.

Well, I must at this point enter two notes of caution. First that, as the authoress of the article herself almost admits, the same applies also to most of the plants Sappho mentions. And second, in this field it would be comparatively easy to persuade the uninitiated of virtually anything.

3. Sappho's view of nature is, as this survey has shown, concentrated on flowering plants. She mentions such plants not less than 40 times, and among them 10 genera can be identified.

These statistics, with only slight reservations about the number of identifiable genera, I happily accept. And so, last, longest, most suggestive and perhaps also most controversial.

4. The plants which Sappho mentions are always common ones. This is certainly due to her being Aeolian. The Aeolians to a certain extent lack the sense

of the unusual and the peculiar that is characteristic of the Ionians. The plants which Sappho mentions all have another characteristic feature in common: they grow in the town or in its surroundings … Herbs which were difficult of access or rarities did not interest her, and she seems to have taken no pains to seek them out. From all we know about Sappho, it appears that she was a typical town dweller, and this is further confirmed by her description of plants. She did not need to move far from the town and its neighbourhood to have opportunities of encountering the flora she depicts.

Because Theocritus is the first Greek poet who demonstrably (see Idyll VII) took long walks into the country, and moreover notices much that he saw on the way, this sharply distinguishes him from all his poetical predecessors, even though each of the three great tragedians, like Homer before them and even Plato after, employs an occasional vivid word or phrase drawn straight from the plant kingdom. In the *Phaedrus* Plato portrays, for the only time in all his writings, Socrates as taking a walk outside the walls of Athens and he mentions two plants that can be confidently identified: 'By Hera this is a delightful retreat. The plane tree here is splendidly spreading and tall, the shade of big Agnos (that is *Vitex agnus-castus*, a common aromatic shrub with blue flowers) is together lovely and, as it is in full flower, it will make the place as fragrant as could be'. Plato, like Sappho, has chosen two plants that would grow just outside the city and has also at least put them in their natural setting on the banks of the Ilissus river.

In one of the above extracts from Ingrid Waern's article, she claims that from the 40 passages in the Sapphic fragments where flowering plants are mentioned '10 genera', in her own words, 'can be identified'. Now three of these 10 genera are unanimously agreed to fall into the botanical family *Umbelliferae*, of which the most familiar wild representative in Britain is the abundant cow-parsley of the roadsides, the most commonly cultivated one either the ordinary crinkly parsley or the carrot. Moreover all three of the umbelliferous plants which Sappho is generally thought to have meant have more or less flat heads consisting of numerous more or less tiny white flowers. The identification of such white-flowered umbellifers, even within, say, a range of five miles from Cambridge, calls either for so well trained an eye or for so detailed a descriptive Flora, that I think it exceedingly doubtful whether, with the whole flora of Greece to choose from, the ancient Greek names for them were either consistently applied or permit of definite identification. The Greek names for the three plants in question are first, ἄνθρυσκον (anthruskon) which in my view defies identification, second ἄνητον or ἄνηθον (aneton or anethon), which may well be our dill, and third σέλινον (in Aeolic σέλιννον) (selinon or selinnon), which is without question, whether wild or cultivated, celery. Such is the superficial similarity between the many white-flowered umbellifers that it matters little which of the various suggested identifications you select. The desired visual effect is just the same, a filmy white veil beside the track.

Two plant names remain to be discussed. The first is ἴον (ion). On the indisputable ground that it is often called μέλαν (melan), Thiselton-Dyer identifies it specifically with the sweet violet, *Viola odorata*, which has dark purple flowers. Here such dogmatism is unwarranted. I fully agree with some sentences from Ingrid Waern which run as follows:

It is reasonable to think of *Viola lesbiaca*, which is very common on Lesbos and is a synonym of the Turkish *Viola kitaibeliana*. This violet … has creamy-white to yellow flowers.

The passage from Sappho in question contains, not the simple name ἴον (ion), but the compound adjective ἰόκολπος (iokolpos), which she applied to a νύμφα (numpha) or bride, implying creamy white rather than dark purple. Thus in a single short paragraph Ingrid Waern has proved a very important point: that the name ἴον, like many another ancient Greek plant name, covers more than one modern botanical species.

A final quotation from her article will introduce the other plant name:

Of κρόκος, the *Crocus*, Sappho gives us only the adjective (fr. 92.7), "dyed with Saffron". Saffron is extracted from *Crocus sativus* … *Crocus sativus*, the saffron crocus, grows wild around the whole Aegean sea. It has lilac-coloured flowers and blossoms in autumn. The stigma is used for making saffron.

The first entry under κρόκος (krokos) in L.S.J., is 'saffron, *Crocus sativus*', which applies to the plant itself; while the second subsection opens with the words

> 2. saffron (made from its stigmas),

and thereafter cites as an example of this sense of the word a lyric passage from Aeschylus, *Agamemnon* 239, in which the relevant words are

> κρόκου βαφὰς δ' ἐς πέδον χέουσα.

This is, I believe, the only passage, and therefore the only sense, in which Aeschylus uses the word at all. But Sophocles, at *Oedipus Coloneus* 685, another lyric passage, writes ὁ δὲ χρυσαυγὴς κρόκος, which is surely correctly taken in L.S.J. to apply to the plant itself and incidentally, the word χρυσαυγὴς is translated 'gold-gleaming'. And to complete the story, Euripides, in yet another lyric passage beginning at *Ion* 889, speaks of κρόκεα πέταλα …χρυσανταυγῆ, the epithet on this occasion translated in L.S.J. as 'reflecting golden light'.

Now, when all this is put together, the same question arises as arose about ἴον: how can the same plant, κρόκος, be said by different authors on different occasions to have 'lilac coloured flowers', to be 'gold-gleaming' and to reflect 'golden light'? And the answer can only be that κρόκος must include more than one species, at least one lilac-coloured and one golden-yellow or orange. But when Theophrastus himself, at the end of chapter 7 of Book VII of the *Historia Plantarum*, writes οὐδὲ ὁ κρόκος οὔτε ὁ εὔοσμος οὔθ᾽ ὁ λευκὸς᾽ οὔθ᾽ ὁ ἀκανθώδης, and thereby casually adds at least another two to the list of species, one white and one thorny, I begin to despair of identifying any of them. Even if we grant, as I hesitate to do, that ὁ εὔοσμος, the fragrant crocus, is the one with lilac-coloured flowers, namely *Crocus sativus*, yet Halácsy's *Conspectus Florae Graecae*, vol. 3 (1904) still leaves us to choose between 3 species of yellow-flowered crocus, 7 of white-flowered, and makes no mention whatever of a thorny one. Thiselton-Dyer, on no other evidence than that of the epithets already given, each of which is applied only in the single passages cited, proceeds, to identify the 'gold-gleaming' crocus with *C. olivieri*, the one 'reflecting golden light' with *C. chrysanthus*, the white one with *C. cancellatus* and the thorny one with a plant as different as could be in most respects from any known crocus, namely safflower or *Carthamus tinctorius*. Of this last, a strapping great thistle, Arthur Hort, who explicitly attributes all his identification to Thiselton-Dyer, says in a footnote:

This plant can only have been called κρόκος because it produced a yellow dye.

a comment which suggests that he was none too happy about this particular identification.

Thiselton-Dyer's *ex cathedra* pronouncements naturally occur at relatively infrequent and irregular intervals throughout the 2111 pages of Liddell and Scott's *Lexicon* but are to be found in the mere 16½ pages on plants which he contributed to the third edition (1916) of *A Companion to Greek Studies*. Nevertheless whenever I consider the undisputed rather than indisputable sway that for more than half a century Thiselton-Dyer has held over this field, I am filled with indignation.

From the day I became interested in the subject I knew enough about it, if only *just* enough, not to be too easily misled. It is on behalf of those numerous scholars and students, who, justifiably taking Thiselton-Dyer's verdicts as final and definitive, have been unwittingly led into consequent error. Should any of you ever find yourself confronted, in whatever Greek text you happen to be studying, with a problem of botanical identification, I earnestly beg you, before you put pen to paper, to remember the wisdom of Socrates.

LECTURE 2

GREEK AGRICULTURAL WRITERS

WILD TULIPS OF CRETE

THEOPHRASTUS' CONTRIBUTIONS TO BOTANY

If we were to judge only from the quantity of ancient literature still extant, we might be excused for assuming that the writing of agricultural treatises was a pastime that appealed more to the Romans than to the Greeks. However, at least two relatively reliable authorities suggest that such a conclusion would be unjustified. Not only does Aristotle, at *Politics* 1258^{b}40, say in so many words: 'For example Cheratides of Paros and Apollodorus of Lemnos have written about agriculture and fruit-farming and similarly others too on other subjects'; even more telling is a passage from Columella, *De Re Rustica* 1,7–11, in which, writing some 400 years later than Aristotle, he gives us the names of no less than 42 Greek authors, sprung from every quarter of the ancient Greek world, who by his time had contributed to an apparently vast bulk of literature on agricultural topics; almost the whole of this has sunk without trace. Hence I can confine my discussion of the passage from Columella to its opening sentence, which runs as follows:

There is a great throng of Greeks who give instruction on husbandry; and the first of them [that is, princeps], that most renowned poet Hesiod of Boeotia, has contributed in no small degree to our art.

Since even Hesiod in the *Works and Days* mentions only a dozen plants in all (as opposed to Homer's 60), we could well afford to ignore the agricultural approach to botany were it not for Theophrastus. Here I feel I must make an autobiographical digression.

My earliest known ancestor was a gardener by profession, and in recent times each of the last four generations has produced more than one member of the family who, whatever their official occupation, indulged whenever possible in one branch or other of natural history with an enthusiasm verging on monomania. My father was a fine example. By profession a theologian, and a Regius Professor at that, he could without exaggeration have been called one of the leading British amateurs in first entomology, next ornithology and finally botany. I too started by collecting butterflies and moths; but, since most of them are to be found only in the vicinity of their food plants, my fervour was first augmented and then largely supplanted by a passion for what I have so far loosely called botany. And that brings me to the very important distinction motivating this digression.

Botany in the strict sense consists of various separable specialised studies, in most of which I am not much interested.

The only such studies of much concern to me are first *taxonomy*, which consists in identifying, naming and classifying plants; second *cytology*, the examination and counting of chromosomes as throwing light both on taxonomy and on evolution (in this field all I do is gratefully accept other people's findings); and third and last and, to me, immeasurably the most absorbing, *ecology*, which means to me what lives and grows with what, and where, and why. So, on the frequent occasions when I am asked why I am interested in botany, I habitually reply that I'm not, I'm interested in *field botany*. To exemplify this I will relate my experience with the tulips of Crete after first studying the published information about them.

There are quite certainly three distinct species of tulips (*Tulipa*) known as wild native plants only in Crete.

As long ago as the spring of 1938, when I was walking from the north coast to the south, through the heart of the White Mountains, I came across quantities of the most local of the three certain species, *Tulipa bakeri*, in its only known station, on the small, oval, upland plain of Omalo.

The few bulbs which, in a torrential downpour, I succeeded in extracting, without a trowel, from the deep red soil, were brought into cultivation, and the vast quantity of the plant which now flourishes, not only in our own garden at Shepreth but also in the National Tulip Collection in the Cambridge Botanic Garden, has sprung, by stolons rather than seed, from those few original bulbs.

Gratified by this success I longed to find the other species. I ransacked the herbaria at Kew and the British Museum (Natural History) and the available literature, but my enquiry added virtually nothing to the information provided by Daniel Hall's *The Genus Tulipa* (1940). According to this *Tulipa cretica* is a rare plant of the mountains; *Tulipa saxatilis* is a lowland species; and finally the latter, being a triploid (which means having one and a half times the normal number of chromosomes), is hence incapable of setting fertile seed and reduced to the unsatisfactory method of self reproduction by forming new bulbs at the end of underground stolons. In March 1971 my wife and I visited Crete. Within three days of our arrival we had not only revisited *Tulipa bakeri* to get our eye in, we had also found a vast colony of *Tulipa saxatilis* and a tolerably large one, though nothing like so large as one we found later at the wrong end of the island, of *Tulipa cretica*. And furthermore – which is the important point – by so doing we conclusively disproved two of those three statements and in my opinion gone a long way towards disproving the third. As subsequent discoveries of other stations confirmed, *T. cretica* regularly grows on bare patches of red soil at altitudes of well under 500 feet; *T. saxatilis* inhabits cliff-ledges and large rocks at an approximate average altitude of 2,000 feet; and finally this latter has a special predilection for small, deep, widely spaced holes in the vertical sides of weathered limestone boulders, which it could not conceivably have reached by underground stolons but could only have colonised by means of fertile seed. I need only add that this opinion has since been triply corroborated. A cytologist at Kew has re-counted the chromosomes of the six bulbs I gave him and found their number to be exactly the same as in almost every other normal species of tulip. Second, two out of three bulbs I gave another expert produced apparently perfectly good seed, which I sent when

it ripened to Kew. And last, and most satisfying of all, another field botanist, who was quite unknown to me, visited Crete in May 1974, followed the directions to our first site which I had published in the *Quarterly Bulletin of the Alpine Garden Society* 40: 188–196, 301–308 (1972), and found that the plant in its native habitat was producing an abundance of seed which conclusively demonstrated its fertility by germinating with exceptional rapidity, and at an exceptionally high percentage, in his garden near Durham. For Theophrastus, however, whom an American historian of botany, Edward Lee Greene (1843–1915), has almost idolatrously called 'the protobotanist', such enquiries had little appeal. Greene appears to have done a good deal more than full justice to Theophrastus in his *Landmarks of Botanical History* (1910) but with his aid I hope to strike a fair balance between opposed prejudices.

Greene ends his account of Theophrastus with a summary 'Recapitulation', in which he lists, each in a separate brief paragraph to itself, what he regards as the protobotanists's chief claims to that title. The following are four typical examples:

9. He indicated the … important differences of the hypogynous, perigynous and epigynous insertion of corolla and androecium.

10. He distinguished between the centripetal and centrifugal in inflorescences.

11. He was first to use the term fruit in the technical sense, as applying to every form and phase of seed encasement, seed included; and gave to carpology the term pericarp.

12. He classified all seed plants as (a) angiospermous and (b) gymnospermous.

The actual passage in the *Historia Plantarum*, in which two of those four momentous discoveries are announced, is not beyond our understanding. It comes from para. 3 of Ch. 13 of Book I. I give it to you *in toto* as rendered by Hort in the Loeb Classical Library.

Here it is:

But there are also differences in the way of growth and the position of the flower; some plants have it close above the fruit, as vine and olive; in the latter, when the flowers drop off, they are seen to have a hole through them, and this men take for a sign whether the tree has blossomed well; for if the flower is burnt up or sodden, it sheds the fruit along with itself, and so there is no hole through it. The majority of flowers have the fruit-case (περικάρπιον) in the middle of them, or, it may be, the flower is on the top of the fruit-case, as in pomegranate apple pear plum and myrtle, and among under-shrubs, in the rose and in the many of the coronary plants. For these have their seeds below, beneath the flower, and this is most obvious in the rose because of the size of the seed-vessel. In some cases again the flower is on the top of the actual seeds, as in pinethistle safflower and all thistle-like plants; for these have a flower attached to each seed. So too with some herbaceous plants, as *anthemon*, and among pot-herbs, with cucumber, gourd and bottle-gourd; all these have the flower attached on top of the fruits, and the flowers persist for a long time while the fruits are developing.

In that relatively short paragraph you have, in simple and non-technical language, first and foremost what Greene calls 'the important differences of the hypogynous, perigynous and epigynous insertion of corolla and androecium', and second, and almost incidentally, the basis for Greene's further statement that Theophrastus 'gave to carpology the term pericarp'.

It would be unreasonable and ungenerous in the extreme to expect from a single short paragraph more than those two quite different innovations. But that same short paragraph does more than that. It raises by implication at least four points of considerable interest and importance. I will begin by summarising them, in simpler language than Greene's in his 'Recapitulation', as follows:

1. By simple lists of plants used to illustrate some point, such as, in this passage, the words 'as in pomegranate apple pear plum and myrtle, and among under-shrubs, in the rose', he just about doubles the number of plants whose names are already to be found in earlier extant literature.
2. Although such lists would obviously be value-less unless the plants listed were already familiar by name to his listeners or readers (thus indicating

that at this elementary level a good deal was already known), he occasionally gives a vivid and easily recognizable description of a plant which was presumably less familiar and therefore needed to be described.
3. Although he seems seldom if ever to have gone out on botanical excursions but to have worked almost exclusively in his garden or study, he gives abundant evidence, like his master Aristotle in the field of zoology, of careful, patient and sometimes acute observation.
4. Although some of the various bases on which, in various contexts, he attempts to classify plants are sensible, natural and, for certain purposes, valuable, he never attempts a formal classification of the modern type based on more or less obvious physical resemblances between one plant and another. This omission is understandable for so early a stage in the history of botany, but it is still irritating in that, by his constant use of adjectives such as ἀκανθῶδες (akanthodes; thistle-like) in the passage under discussion to denote plants showing just these resemblances, he reveals that he possessed the insight with which he might so easily have developed a formal classification on the approved modern lines. Both the originality and the influence of these achievements, as well as their intrinsic merits and defects, deserve much more attention.

Fortunately the first of my four points calls for only two additions. In round numbers, the extant works of Greek authors before Theophrastus name approximately 250 plants between them; Theophrastus alone names some 500. However a considerable proportion of this total defies identification.

It is to be noted in the first place that from the simple lists of plant names (in which, incidentally, Theophrastus reveals a strong predilection for trinities like 'tamarisk, willow, alder' or 'palm, squill, asphodel' in *H.P.* 1. 4. 3), one can deduce, first, that to his listeners and readers, most of the plants he names were already familiar enough, and second, that those earlier writers who mentioned plants at all did so for motives quite other than botanical and cannot therefore be taken to give any clue whatever to the number of plants already with popular and widely accepted names. And regarding those relatively few plants which, to Theophrastus' mind, were so generally *unfamiliar* as to call for a description, I give you first an actual example drawn, again *verbatim*, from Hort's translation of the *Historia*.

In the course of an altogether admirable description of the elder tree (*Sambucus*) in chapter 13.4 of Book III, we can discern in the following sentences the next two of Theophrastus' characteristics that call for comment:

The single leaflet is soft and oblong, like the leaf of a broad-leaved bay, but larger, broader, and rounder at the middle and base, though it narrows more to a point at the tip and is jagged all round. The whole leaf is composed of leaflets growing about a single thick fibrous stalk, to which they are attached at either side, in pairs at each joint, with one attached at the tip of the stalk. The leaves are somewhat reddish, porous and fleshy. The whole is shed in one piece, wherefore one may consider that the whole structure is really a leaf.

This very faithful description affords an admirable illustration of my next two points. First, the clear distinction between the leaflets of a compound leaf and the leaf as a whole makes it plain that:

Theophrastus was well beyond the elementary stage of botany. At the same time he obviously suffers, here as elsewhere, from the total lack of even the simplest technical vocabulary, nor does he often see fit to repair that deficiency. Hence the significance that Greene attaches to the introduction of the word περικάρπιον (perikarpion). Indeed this particular passage even illustrated his simple but quite ingenious way out of the difficulty. Since he cannot describe a leaf, as a modern botanist would, as, say ovate or lanceolate, he takes any one of 5 or 6 leaves that would be familiar to all his public – in this case the broad-leaved bay – as his standard of comparison and describes other less familiar types of leaf by simultaneously comparing and contrasting them with the most

appropriate of these standards. Thus, for instance, instead of 'ovate' Theophrastus writes 'like a pear leaf', and so on. The result, as in this case, is often graphic and precise enough.

My general impression is that Theophrastus had little taste for botanical field studies. He writes of plants in general (*H.P.* I.14. 4):

But most of the wild have no names and few know about them, while most of the cultivated kinds have received names and they are more commonly observed.

On the basis of this remark many hypotheses have been formulated. Thus Kurt Sprengel (in Hort's words 'a better botanist than scholar' who 'made the first comprehensive attempt to determine in modern nomenclature the plants mentioned by Theophrastus') maintained in his translation and commentary of 1822 that the observations even of the Greek flora which Theophrastus records were not first hand; but, to quote Hort again, 'Kirchner, in an able tract, combats the contention'. In more recent times even Greene, that most ardent of admirers, admits in so many words that

As for Theophrastus, out of the some 500 species and varieties of plants of which he treats, only an insignificant proportion are other than domestic,

but he immediately goes on to argue, again *verbatim*, that

To have assigned space in his book for the consideration of many wild plants must have appeared like a marked innovation; one that indeed looked in the direction of a widening of the field of botanical investigation, and was therefore of promise for the future of the science; but it must have given occasion for carping critics to ask how wild plants, such as have neither names nor history, are entitled to a place in the History of Plants.

And finally Hort himself voices his own conjectures in his introduction:

Now at this period the Peripatetic School must have been a very important educational institution; Diogenes says that under Theophrastus it numbered 2,000 pupils … May we not hazard a guess that a number of the students were appropriately employed in the collection of facts and observations? The assumption that a number of 'travelling students' were so employed would at all events explain certain references in Theophrastus' botanical works. He says constantly 'The Macedonians say', 'The men of Mount Ida say' and so forth. Now it seems hardly probable that he is quoting from written treatises by Macedonian or Idaean writers. It is at least a plausible suggestion that in such references he is referring to reports of the districts in question contributed by students of the school.

These learned pundits, anyhow, seem agreed in subscribing to the general opinion that Theophrastus himself evinces no great enthusiasm for first-hand field studies. But I will still venture to hazard a further conjecture. There are occasional passages in the *History* which read to me – and here I can for once speak from a good deal of first-hand experience – exactly like the kind of field notes which many botanists to this day scribble on the spot and may or may not doll up into intelligible prose on their return from an excursion. The following two suggest to me that Theophrastus sometimes did travel quite far from home and observe for himself as he travelled; other passages convey the same impression about parts of mainland Greece as well.

The first passage, consisting of paras. 7 to 9 of chapter 6 of Book II, comes from the middle of quite a long discussion on the various kinds of date-palm and their fruit. Para. 7 opens with three sentences on the so-called 'royal palm', of which the last two run as follows:

but this, they say, is rare; it grows hardly anywhere except in the park of the ancient Bagoas, near Babylon.

and there, as the word λέγουσι makes quite clear, Theophrastus' information is at best second-hand. But immediately thereupon follow two whole paragraphs on three other species of palm, of each of which Theophrastus tells us, among other things, that it grows in Cyprus, without the faintest hint that he is here relying on anybody else's observations than his own. And when in para. 9, after one further apparently first-hand remark on the peculiar forking of the palms in Egypt, he proceeds to tell us (and correctly too) that those in

Crete can have as many as five heads, the very first word of this new sentence is his favourite φάσιν. This Cretan palm is now known as *Phoenix theophrasti* Greuter.

But when we find, as we do, that in the second passage exactly the same phenomenon recurs at much greater length and much more prominently, the proposition becomes a bit less tentative. In Book IV, which as a whole is headed by Hort 'Of the trees and plants special to particular districts and positions', and which can therefore be fairly regarded as the prototype both of ecological and of topographical botany, ch. 2, 'of the trees special to Egypt, and of the carob', is separated from ch. 8, 'Of the plants of rivers, marshes, and lakes, especially in Egypt', by five chapters devoted respectively to the supposedly special plants of Libya, Asia and northern regions, and to the aquatic plants of first the Mediterranean and then what Theophrastus terms 'the outer sea'. I should be surprised if anybody reading Book IV, for the first time were not immediately struck by the contrast, chiefly but not solely stylistic, between the apparently first-hand accounts of Egypt and the parts of Libya other than the desert and the avowedly second-hand reports of all the remaining districts. I cite only one example of this contrast, which comes from the middle of Chapter 3, the first three paragraphs of which, like the whole preceding chapter on the trees of Egypt, give every appearance of recording, in direct speech, Theophrastus' own observations and impressions.

Para. 4 then opens abruptly with the word Ἔνιοι, with φάσιν or λέγουσι clearly understood, and proceeds to give, in the usual accusative and infinitive construction, a postscript to the account of the Egyptian tree called λωτός (lotos) in paras. 1 and 2.

Schneider, following Scaliger, actually went so far as to exchange the positions of paras. 3 and 4 so as to make the account of the λωτός continuous. But to my mind this proposal is for two reasons utterly misguided. In the first place it destroys the present obvious and instantaneous transition from first to second-hand reporting. And second, it leaves wholly unexplained the otherwise unaccountable fact that the whole of par. 5, which is again very clearly second-hand, again employs the accusatives and infinitives of reported speech. Largely but not wholly on grounds of syntax such as this, I am prepared to believe that, though he probably never went to Crete and certainly never to mainland Asia, Theophrastus had actually, at some stage before he wrote the *Historia*, visited both Cyprus and Egypt, including the less arid parts of Libya.

Perhaps the most remarkable fact about this seemingly obvious but revolutionary conjecture is that, as far as I can discover, nobody has propounded it before. If my hypothesis could be shown to contain a germ of truth, it would appreciably enhance my regard for Theophrastus by giving to his botanical researches a less arid, less academic and more human aspect. Nevertheless there can still be no contesting the general view that he conducted by far the greater part of those researches within the confines of the Lyceum and its garden. And in that garden he studied not only the various characteristics and behaviour of many different plants, he also embraced within his studies some of the basic principles of horticulture and incorporated his findings mainly in Book II of the *Historia*. To this day some of those findings make unexpectedly fascinating reading and might even teach an expert gardener a thing or two. I can give here only a few brief examples, all from this Book.

1. The plants chosen ... should be taken from soil resembling that in which you are going to plant them, or else inferior. The holes should be dug as long as possible beforehand, and should always be deeper than the original holes, even for those whose roots do not run very deep. (*H.P.* II.5. 1).

2. (II.5. 7). *ib.* §7 Nor should one fail to note what soil suits each variety even of those closely related. There is the greatest difference, one may say, between the different kinds of vine: for they say there are as many kinds of vine as there are of soil. If they are planted as their nature requires, they turn out well, if otherwise, they are unfruitful. And these remarks apply almost equally to all trees.

3. (II.7. 4). Manure does not suit all alike, nor is the same manure equally good for all. Some need it pungent, some less so, some need it quite light. The most pungent is human dung, ... pig-manure second to it, goat-manure third, fourth that of sheep, fifth that of oxen, and sixth that of beasts of burden.

4. (II.7. 6). If a tree does not bear fruit but inclines to a leafy growth, they split that part of the stem which is underground and insert a stone corresponding to the crack thus made, and then, they say, it will bear. The same result follows if one cuts off some of the roots, and accordingly they thus treat the surface roots of the vine when it runs to leaf. In the case of figs, in addition to root-pruning, they also sprinkle ashes about the tree, and make gashes in the stems, and then, they say, it bears better.

5. The fig progresses more quickly, and is less eaten by grubs, if the cutting is set in a squill-bulb; in fact anything so planted is vigorous and grows faster.

I do not know if any gardener has ever tested in recent times this primitive method of stimulating root growth. The ancient Greek σκίλλα (skilla) is not any species placed nowadays in *Scilla*, but is the plant now known as *Urginea maritima* (*Scilla maritima*, Linnaeus), whose tall, slender and elegant spikes of starry white flowers rise in autumn, before the leaves appear, from those enormous bulbs so shallowly embedded in the soil that you often find them in Greece, usually not far from the sea, lying altogether detached on the surface like great croquet balls.

Above I have credited Theophrastus with a capacity for patient, careful and sometimes acute observation. About the best possible illustration of that capacity comes from the beginning of Book VIII chapter 2 of the *Historia* and describes the different ways in which different kinds of seeds germinate.

In germinating, some plants produce their roots and their leaves from the same point, some separately from either end of the seed. Wheat, barley, and in general all the cereals produce them from either end, in a manner corresponding to the position of the seed in the ear, the root growing from the stout lower part, the shoot from the upper part, so that the root and the stem form a single continuous whole. But beans and other leguminous plants do not grow in the same manner, but produce the root and the stem from the same point, namely the point at which the seed is attached to the pod, which is already a sort of starting point of fresh growth …

Barley and wheat come up with a single leaf, but peas, beans, and chick-peas have more than one. All leguminous plants have a single woody root, and also slender side-roots springing from this … But wheat, barley and the other cereals have many fine roots which are therefore matted. Again, all such plants have many branches and many stems, but there is a sort of contrast between these two classes. The leguminous plants, which have a single root, have many side-growths from the stem above; while the cereals, which have many roots, send up many shoots but these have no side-shoots …

Well, that passage, in which once again the details are perfectly accurate, brings out just the qualities in Theophrastus that I wish to stress. In the first place he clearly had great patience; he could not have reached the conclusions he here summarises without repeated observations of the often quite slow process of germination of a considerable number of different seeds. Second, he was a careful worker; in his account of the various kinds of roots, the description of what he calls the 'slender side-roots' (ἀποφύσεις λεπταί) could never have been attained by hasty or clumsy work. Third, his habitual quest for generalisations has in this instance led him, in the sentence 'Barley and wheat come up with a single leaf, but peas, beans and chick-peas with more than one', to a fundamental distinction still regarded as dividing flowering plants into two great classes, the monocotyledons and the dicotyledons. But this same passage reveals also two equally clear deficiencies, one of them admittedly not his fault, which are bound to have affected all his botanical research. When, very early on in his treatise (I. 1. 11) he lists the external organs of a tree as 'root, stem, branch, bud, leaf, flower, fruit', and soon after, passing to the internal structure, writes: 'plants are made up of bark, wood and pith', he reveals at once, by his deliberate exclusion of such non-essential parts as thorns or tendrils, a grasp of the essential and, by his division between the external and internal parts, an understanding of the distinction between morphological and anatomical organography which, as Greene emphasises, is quite remarkable in such a pioneer. But none the less, owing to the total absence then of visual aids such as even a magnifying glass, most of his work in this and related fields is gravely impaired by his ignorance of such minute but vitally important elements in a plant as cells or chromosomes. The fact that his research on germination could be much more conveniently conducted in the shelter of the garden than in the open countryside underlines once again that same disinclination for field studies which debarred him from blazing an adequate trail into the virtually uncharted fields, where no microscope would have been needed, of botanical topography and ecology.

Like Herodotus before him, Theophrastus was well aware that date-palm trees were either male or female. From prehistoric times the practice had been adopted, as Theophrastus describes in the final paragraph of Book II, of fertilisation of the female tree by scattering over it the pollen from a flowering branch of a male tree. But, although accordingly he is often elsewhere disposed to attribute sex to plants, we eventually find that he usually attributes sexual differences merely in a metaphorical way to two distinct species, occasionally to fertile and sterile varieties of the same species, and very rarely to those relatively few so-called 'dioecious' species in which whole specimens, rather than separable parts of the same specimen, are indeed either male or female. It is indeed obvious that like other botanists down to the 17th century A.D. he has no idea of the sexual nature or function of those organs, such as the stamens, the pistils or the ovary, which are actually involved. We might have hoped that a philosopher-naturalist of Theophrastus' calibre would have been led by his knowledge of the date-palm to a more realistic generalisation of the sexual nature of all flowers. But no.

This question of sexual distinctions in the plant kingdom leads on to taxonomy and classification, in which Theophrastus' various attempts to find a satisfactory basis call for fuller treatment. As is evident from the passage in which, by his mention of a group of plants which he terms ἀκανθώδη (akanthode) or 'thistle-like', he was not blind to the natural affinities which, in some families at least, are manifest even to the untrained eye. Several such natural groups he actually names – the καλαμώδη (kalamode) for instance, including all grasses, the βολβώδη (bolbode) including all bulbous plants, and more precisely, the ναρθηκ-ώδη (narthekode) or fennel-like plants, which are simply the *Umbelliferae*, the cow-parsley family, already mentioned in connection with Sappho. At times, he lets his awareness of these natural affinities override his more artificial methods of classification. Thus, for instance, by the similarity he perceived between the seed heads of poppies and of water-lilies he abandoned his usual practice of grouping plants together according to their type of habitat and passed in his discussion directly from the one to the other.

At different times and in different contexts he attempts different systems of classification. He divides plants sometimes into the wild and the cultivated – a distinction which, as he tells us at *H.P.* I.3. 5, a predecessor called Hippon would not admit and of which he is himself, in theory at least, very sceptical; sometimes into flowering and flowerless or fruit-bearing and fruitless; sometimes into terrestrial, marsh-loving, aquatic and marine; and most often of all, into trees, shrubs, sub-shrubs and herbs. Each of these artificial methods

which he deliberately adopts is, unfortunately, much less defensible than his instinctive recognition of natural groupings. Even his distinction between trees, shrubs, sub-shrubs and herbs, which seems perhaps the most plausible of them all, comes an ugly cropper, for instance, over a family like the *Leguminosae*, which contains a whole range of familiar plants from the laburnum and judas tree, through gorse and broom, beans and peas, down to clover. And the sad result is that Theophrastus' taxonomy is always far more scientific when he unthinkingly follows his natural instincts than when, as he usually does, he allows himself time to think. I am tempted to conclude that the unwitting villain of the piece was none other than Theophrastus', friend, patron and master, Aristotle himself, with his emphasis on logic.

However the actual unwitting injustice Aristotle did Theophrastus is that in every respect Aristotle so far outshone him, as indeed he would have outshone almost anybody else, that even in their specialised researches in zoology and botany respectively the contrast is discernible between a powerful and penetrating mind and a plodding and pedantic mind. Indeed, to divulge at last an opinion which hitherto, by my choice of examples of his writings, I have done my utmost to conceal, I find Theophrastus' botanical treatises boring, admittedly not the opinion of others who have studied them.

Lecture 3

Naming of Plants

Plants of Theocritus

Location of Hylas' Pool on Cos

Plants Depicted in Minoan Art

Consideration of the traditional naming of plants in ancient times is highly relevant not only to the study of the works of Theophrastus and Dioscorides but equally to every other author, earlier or later, poet or prose-writer, Greek or Roman, who ever mentioned a plant.

Nowadays botanists have universally agreed that every species of plant must be known by a binomial (or two-word) name of Latin form even though derived from Greek or another language. This system is now regulated by an international code of botanical nomenclature which aims to ensure that no two species have the same name and that the same name is used all the world over. But the binomial system as consistently used in modern botany (thereby distinct from its incidental use much earlier) is relatively modern, its introduction being perhaps the chief claim to lasting renown of the 18th century Swedish naturalist Carl Linnaeus. Theophrastus, just as he had no technical terms to hand, had no technical nomenclature either; he simply accepted the popular one-word names already attached to a number of plants. It is admittedly surprising how many of the names used by Theophrastus retain, by many and devious routes in addition to mere oral tradition, a permanent place in botanical nomenclature. Thus under the one letter A in an Index to Theophrastus' *Historia Plantarum* there are no less than 17 plant names, including such old friends as *Anemone*, *Arum* and *Asparagus*, which persist to this day as the names of botanical genera. But whereas today each such generic name needs to have a specific epithet added before it can precisely signify one kind of plant and one only, Theophrastus apparently often applies the single name to a single kind of plant. Probably this age-old procedure led Thiselton-Dyer to believe over-confidently that he could identify precisely every plant mentioned in extant Greek literature with a single species having now an exclusive specific name. But, as a consequence of this same habit, a single ancient Greek name, like many a popular name today, often proves, as Thiselton-Dyer himself tacitly acknowledged in his treatment of κρόκος (krokos) but not of ἴον (ion), to cover a wide variety of what are now regarded as separate species. The result is, of course, that very many of the plants named and even some of those described by Theophrastus are forever impossible, like the prickly crocus, to identify by anything more than a hazardous guess.

Theophrastus was, like his master Aristotle, a bold but patient pioneer in a hitherto virtually untrodden field; despite my criticisms, he has a good claim to his title of 'Father of Botany'. However even in his chosen field he left more work of a pioneering nature to be done by his successors than did Aristotle in the field of zoology. But looking to the future, what was the influence of Theophrastus on his successors? And in particular, what influence if any did he exercise on Theocritus? A preliminary answer to that question can be lifted *verbatim* from an article in 1937 by Alice Lindsell:

'Most of the wild plants have no names, and few know about them', says Theophrastus. How, then, does Theocritus know about them? What has happened? Surely just Theophrastus himself. His dates are c. 370–285 B.C., so if Theocritus was born in c. 310 B.C., that makes him 25 at the time of Theophrastus' death. So there is nothing anachronistic in attributing botanical knowledge to Theocritus.

These sentences come from her article 'Was Theocritus a botanist?' in *Greece and Rome* [see p. 65 below]. This clearly entailed much work, in the countryside of both Cos and Sicily as well as in her library. Its main thesis strikes me as fundamental and convincing, for Alice Lindsell, like Ingrid Waern, has put her knowledge of field botany to constructive and helpful use.

Nobody doubts that Theocritus came from

Sicily; he was apparently the son of Syracusan parents called Praxagoras and Philinna. The question at issue, until lately a very vexed one, is how long he stayed in his native island and how much of his poetry, if any, he actually wrote there.

Alice Lindsell seems to me to have shown conclusively, from a study of Theocritus' references to plants that, whatever part of the ancient Greek world he had in mind, he filled in the minor details of his scenes – his trees, his shrubs and his flowers – from his own observations, if not in Cos itself which is the explicit background to his one and only bucolic masquerade, Idyll VII, at any rate in a Mediterranean region far to the east of Sicily. He mentions in all, and chiefly in the bucolic idylls, no less than 87 different plants, many more than in the whole of Homer. He is, moreover, relatively seldom content merely to name them: in his choice of descriptive epithets, such as ἀπαλαν (apalan) of a poppy rather than the conventional μέλαινα (melaina) or πολύγναμπτον (polygnampton) of a wild celery leaf, and even more by his invariably placing his plants in their right natural habitat, he shows that he was a genuine and keen observer.

Now, the flora of Greece and of the East Aegean Islands differs widely from that of Sicily and Italy, being much closer to the West Asiatic than to the typically European flora; and its most characteristic element, scarcely to be found in Sicily at all, consists of the spinous aromatic shrubs of those familiar steep, rocky and stony slopes which are known collectively as either the 'maquis' or the 'garigue'. Of the twelve commonest plants of the Greek maquis Theocritus shows himself familiar with as many as ten; a state of affairs almost if not quite inconceivable if he were really writing his poetry in Sicily but perfectly natural, indeed almost inevitable, if he were writing of Sicily in Cos. The plane tree for example – the πλατάνος (platanos) of the ancients, now significantly *Platanus orientalis* – is an Asiatic species, which reaches the westernmost limit of natural distribution in Greece; and likewise the cypress, however characteristic it may now seem of Italy and Sicily,

was originally introduced from further to the East and is unlikely to have grown in Sicily in Theocritus' time. Similarly too, the constant mention of barley and its products – κρίθη, ἄλφιτα, μᾶζα (krithe, alphita, maza) to the virtual exclusion of wheat strongly suggests the stony, barren patches of the eastern Mediterranean rather than the celebrated cornlands of Sicily. So on all these grounds we can accept Miss Lindsell's contention that Theocritus must have spent the more creative part of his life not in Sicily but on Cos.

There are only three paragraphs in her whole article which I find wholly or largely unacceptable on botanical grounds. One is [see p. 67 below]:

"The marshy lake where all things grow in beauty" *because* [her italics for emphasis] they are by water, for rest-harrow and flea-bane cannot grow away from water, … and the poet-botanist has mentioned the fact in the one word "Stomalimnos".

In my opinion on grounds of syntax the reference here should not be to the Stomalimnon but to the river.

To the ecologist this should be a matter of some import. For instead of a saltmarsh, with its highly distinctive vegetation, he has to imagine the flora of a lush river bank, and this change of habitat can hardly fail to affect his identification of the three plants named in the following line. If κνύζα (knuza) in particular is really, as is generally supposed, a species of fleabane, the species in one locality will probably be quite different from that in the other.

It is not however with κνύζα that I am now concerned, but with our old friend αἰγίπυρος (aigipurus); for this is of course the very line that I discussed in that connexion in my first lecture. I am not altogether surprised that Miss Lindsell accepts the identification of αἰγίπυρος with rest-harrow, *Ononis antiquorum*; nearly everybody does. What astonishes me is that she, usually a reliable botanist, should write of it, as she does, that 'rest-harrow … cannot grow away from water'. This is not only an untruth; it can so easily be exposed as such. In his characteristically concise fashion, Halácsy describes the usual habitat of *Ononis antiquorum* as follows:

In incultis, arvis, ruderatis, campis regionis inferioris per totam Graeciam.

In an author who never fails to include the word 'humidis' whenever appropriate (as he uses it, for instance, in describing the habitat of the plant with which Theocritus' κνύζα is regularly identified, namely *Inula graveolens* [now *Dittrichia graveolens*]), that description alone, to which the word 'aridis' could fairly have been added, is sufficient refutation.

The first and last sentences of another paragraph, to which I take objection on, run thus [p. 66 below]:

In the case of ἄγρωστις (Dog's-tooth Grass, *Cynodon dactylon*) Theocritus uses a very botanical epithet "εἰλιτενής", 'creeping in the marsh'; ... I call εἰλιτενής a botanical as opposed to a merely descriptive epithet, because of course the roots are not visible, so it seems likely that Theocritus handled the plant as a specimen ...

That kind of too seldom used argument carries weight with me, εἰλιτενής (eilitenes), is indeed 'a botanical as opposed to a merely descriptive epithet' the nearest modern equivalent of which is, I suppose, the familiar specific epithet *stolonifera*. Indeed εἰλιτενής would have the advantage over *stolonifera* in that, by specifying a marsh as the habitat where the plant creeps, it is at the same time *both* botanical and descriptive. But, alas, Miss Lindsell, having hit upon so promising a line of argument, proceeds to use it only to mislead. Halácsy's description of *Cynodon dactylon* itself opens with the significant and encouraging words, 'rhizomate repente, stolonifero', but his description of its habitat opens discouragingly 'in incultis arenosis, ad vias'. Though *Cynodon dactylon* unquestionably creeps, a marsh is the very last place where you would ever find it so doing. Miss Lindsell's blunder is more regrettable because another grass is an obvious and preferable candidate for the name ἄγρωστις (agrostis). Halácsy's description of it opens this time with the words

'stolonifera; culmis basi decumentibus, ad nodos inferiores saepe radicantibus' – in other words it roots as it creeps – 'in humidis regionis inferioris et montanae'. Its modern botanical name is *Agrostis stolonifera*!

The two names σέλινον (selinon) and ἄγρωστις (agrostis) occur in the same passage of Theocritus, the description in the middle of Idyll XIII of the pool into which the suddenly love-stricken nymphs dragged young Hylas. This is how it runs:

Τάχα δέ κράναν ἐνόησεν
ἡμένῳ ἐν χώρῳ· περὶ δέ θρύα πολλὰ πεφύκει,
κυάνεον τε χελιδόνιον χλωρόν τ᾽ ἀδίαντον
καὶ θάλλοντα σέλινα καὶ εἰλιτένης ἄγρωστις.

Apart from the regular mistranslation of ἄγρωστις as dog's tooth grass, Andrew Gow's rendering suits my purposes well enough:

Soon in a low-lying place he spied a spring, round which grew rushes thick, and dark celandine, green maiden-hair and wild celery luxuriant and creeping dog's-tooth.

I will first describe the pool in some detail. The water is crystal clear and, considering that the pool occupies only a shallow depression, unexpectedly deep in the middle; you cannot see into the depths because of the constant ripple on the surface caused by a tiny waterfall which splashes over the damp ledges of a shelving rock into the head of the pool. Below the fall, however, the little stream immediately spreads out, thanks to the depression in the ground, to form a pool, one bank of which is a low but steep slope with a few rocks cropping out through the quite short grass, the other, in striking contrast, a flat and luxuriant bog with a quantity of tangled grass fringing the pool and actually spreading out here and there right into the water, so that it is hard to say where pool ends and bog begins. Altogether a most attractive place; it is no wonder that here the nymphs gathered to dance and Hylas hastened to dip in his pitcher for Heracles' and Telamon's picnic supper. To visit it, go to the village of Zia on the lower slopes of Mount Dikeon in Cos, and follow one of the little rivulets flowing northwards from there until, converging with others on its way, it debouches into the sea near the salt-pans at Alikes. My reasoning for this conclusion is as follows:

1. The water must be 'crystal-clear'. Had it been otherwise, neither would the nymphs have chosen to sport in it, nor Hylas to draw thence his exigent master's drinking water.

2. It must also be unexpectedly deep, because otherwise, with all those nymphs in it, plus, now, Hylas, a head or two must inevitably have spoilt the whole effect by protruding.

3. Even so, however, there must have been a constant ripple on the surface, because otherwise any passer-by, Heracles included, must inevitably have seen the amorous antics enacted beneath.

4. The waterfall is essential to account not only for the constant ripple but also, and perhaps more tellingly, for the presence of ἀδίαντον (adianton), a delicate fern of a pale yellowish-green colour – precisely – χλωρόν (chloron) in fact, as opposed to κυάνεον (χελιδόνιον) [kuaneon (chelidonion)], with an exclusive insistence on growing, as Halácsy puts it, 'in umbrosis humidis, speluncis, stillicidiis'. Incidentally, the botanical name of this fern is *Adiantum capillus-veneris*.

5. Likewise the low grassy bank on one side of the pool is virtually indispensable to accommodate the χελιδόνιον (chelidonion), or lesser celandine, *Ranunculus ficaria*, the dark leaves of which contrast with the pale yellowish-green of the *Adiantum*.

Admittedly in ancient Greece two distinct plants were called χελιδόνιον, one μέγα (mega) and one μικρόν (mikron), and moreover they are today in England popularly known as the greater and the lesser celandine. But not only do they belong to entirely different families, Papaveraceae and Ranunculaceae, they look entirely different too. Had Theocritus here meant the greater celandine, which he could not anyhow have done, knowing that it could not occur in the plant community he describes, he not only easily could but inevitably would have written, not κυάνεον τε χελιδόνιον,

which is apt enough for the lesser celandine, but γλαύκιζον τε χελιδόνιον, which would be equally apt for the greater.

The almost level boggy margin on the other side would naturally be dominated by clumps of rushes, θρύα πολλά (thrua polla); it would be fringed at the water's edge by tangled mats of the creeping *Agrostis stolonifera*; and, in certain conditions at least, the clumps of rushes would naturally be overtopped by the vigorous upsurging wild celery, θάλλοντα σέλινα (thallonta selina).

6. As soon as you start down your chosen rivulet from Zia which you will probably find channelled between low rocky grassy banks, you cannot fail to notice quantities of an exceptionally fine form of κυάνεον χελιδόνιον, the lesser celandine, and thereafter, if you keep your eyes open, you should have little difficulty in spotting the rest of Theocritus' list. You will not come upon his pool till you near the end of your walk. First, I doubt whether Hylas, in his quest for drinking water, would have needed to go very far from the seaside meadow where the Argonauts had encamped – a meadow, incidentally, which bore an abundance of the utterly appropriate βούτομος (boutomos) or sedge and κύπειρος (kupeiros) or galingale. And second, Halácsy is, as usual, perfectly correct when, he describes the habitat of wild celery, *Apium graveolens*, as 'In fossis, paludosis, *ad litora maris*'.

This seems to me to establish beyond any doubt the truth of Miss Lindsell's cardinal contention. Even if not a field botanist of high calibre, Theocritus possessed an interest in and a knowledge of wild plants without precedent in the whole range of early Greek literature. Whether or not he owed this interest to the influence of Theophrastus is a different question; I myself again incline to agree with Miss Lindsell that he did.

The last paragraph from her admirable article which invites criticism concerns the plant known to the ancient Greeks as ὑάκινθος (hyakinthos), a name which still, provided only it is given inverted commas, is probably best rendered 'hyacinth'.

The name ὑάκινθος, then, like χελιδόνιον, seems in antiquity to have denoted two quite different plants. Indeed Theophrastus himself explicitly distinguishes between the two when, in *H.P.* VI.8. 2, he tells us that all the wild flowers used by garland-makers are short-lived: πλήν τῆς ὑακίνθου καὶ τῆς ἀγρίας καὶ τῆς σπαρτῆς· αὕτη δὲ διάμενει.

Now Miss Lindsell merely follows the prevailing fashion when she identifies the wild 'hyacinth' with the blue bulbous *Scilla bifolia*, the cultivated 'hyacinth', if only tentatively, with the larkspur, *Delphinium ajacis*. But in my opinion she has very little justification, if any, when she writes a few lines lower down [see p. 68 below]:

> The wild larkspur, being cultivated, grows in meadows, which, in a mountainous land such as Greece, would be low-lying. This is Theocritus' γραπτὰ ὑάκινθος and it is mentioned in Idyll X where the setting is cornfields and flower borders: again unobtrusively right.

Andrew Gow, in a highly informative note on the same line, 28, is rightly more cautious. 'These flowers', he begins, '(for more than one seems to have borne the name), after long discussion, have not been satisfactorily identified'. And he ends by summarising, with due acknowledgement and qualified approval, my own considered opinion that the 'wild hyacinth' was *Orchis quadripunctata*, a widespread and common species of orchid in Greece, very variable in colour, but always bearing on the lip of the flower from two to four darker spots which could easily be imagined as letters of the alphabet.

Here I must emphasize that all the criticisms I have made of Miss Lindsell's invaluable article are alike directed against what, to me, are flagrant misidentifications of ancient Greek plant names; and those misidentifications are the work, not of Miss Lindsell herself, but of Sir William Thiselton-Dyer. There is here a moral for us all. Even those rare scholars capable of combining originality with reliability may sometimes be dazzled by the glare of the specialist expert into errors as unpredictable as, once perpetrated, they appear uncharacteristic and unworthy.

If it is legitimate to use 'an Etruscan stamnos of the early fourth century', as proposed by Gow, to help us identify a plant repeatedly mentioned by Greek writers from Homer onwards, what other light, if any, do the finds of archaeologists throw on the subject of these lectures? Since I have the strongest possible support, that of Professor Cook, for my suspicion that any plants used for decorative purposes by Greek artists of the classical period were imaginary rather than actual, and since any that may be adduced from Hellenistic art are too isolated to yield any general information at all, that question rapidly boils down to the much narrower and more specific one, what can be learnt on the subject from Minoan art?

Some statements all too often thrown out in passing as if they were axiomatic, I can only think are inferences, drawn by their authors from the work of Sir Arthur Evans on the Palace of Minos. I have selected two such statements from the articles of Ingrid Waern and Alice Lindsell. In her 'Flora Sapphica', Ingrid Waern writes:

> Furthermore, there is no evidence to contradict the view that cultivated decorative plants were common on Lesbos at the time. We know that there were such plants in Crete as early as the Minoan Age.

And Alice Lindsell remarks more explicitly to the same effect:

> Fourteen hundred years before him (i.e. Theocritus) Minoan painters looked at plants with his eyes: except for them he is unique in Greek history.

Not only have several pots come to light at Knossos, some of them embellished with a formal and conventional design of leafy reed stems, whose perforated bottoms strongly suggest that they were flower-pots, but also one of the fragments of the so-called Saffron Gatherer fresco depicts two such pots, of a broad and shallow type still widely used for growing bulbs and seeds, actually fulfilling their proper function. What kinds of decorative plants did the Minoans grow in these pots and whence came those plants? I can give only summary and partial answers, and even these call for a prefatory warning in large part taken *verbatim* from a reliable source. In the *Catalogue of Plates* in *Sir Arthur Evans' Knossos Fresco Atlas*, by Cameron and Hood, the following sentences relate to the Saffron Gatherer fresco:

Evans restored the figure as a blue boy ... But it was interpreted as a monkey by Pendlebury ... Platon has regrouped the fragments as a monkey ... For an alternative scheme of restoration with a monkey, see W. Stevenson Smith ...

and so on. When even the central figure can be interpreted by the experts either as a blue boy or as a tame monkey in harness, how can we be sure that what has hitherto been called a crocus is not really, e.g., a tulip? This caveat is uppermost in my mind when I present the following summary of my conclusions, based only on published photographs and drawings rather than on the original artefacts.

Plant paintings in Minoan art, like plant names in Greek literature, seem to fall into three categories: those which justify a confident identification, those which permit only a reasonable conjecture and those on which, granted only a nodding acquaintance with the most familiar of Greek flowers, one guess is as good as another. On this basis there are, I believe, very few plant paintings in the whole sum of Sir Arthur Evans' discoveries, that fall squarely into the first category; marking as generously as I can, I cannot award more than 8 Firsts in all. My Firsts, with references to the most convincing reproductions in Evans' book *The Palace of Minos* are as follows:

1. Saffron Crocus, *Crocus sativus*, actually much better in fig. 271 on p. 459 of Vol. II than in the 'Saffron Gatherer fresco' on Plate 1 of the *Atlas*.
2. Sand Lily, *Pancratium maritimum*, Vol. II, Pl. 11, the so-called 'Panel with Blue Bird' in the 'House of the Frescoes', Plate 17 and *passim*, always very stiff and formal.
3. Cretan Iris, *Iris cretensis*, 2 clumps at the bottom of the same Panel. Plates 17, 18.
4. Ivy, *Hedera helix*, Vol. II, pl. 10, facing p. 447 – again stiff and formal.

5. Papyrus, *Cyperus papyrus*, best in Vol. II, p. 401, fig. 231.
6. Palm trees, *Phoenix theophrasti*, clearest in Vol. II, p. 496; by no means certainly but probably this recently distinguished endemic Cretan species.
7. Madonna Lily, *Lilium candidum*, *passim*, notably Pl. VIII, fig. 1, of the *Atlas*.

Next come two plants, olive and myrtle. There are many Minoan paintings where one or other of the two is represented but it is not certain which. Since however there is at least one fresco, Pl. VIII, fig. 3 in the Atlas which unquestionably portrays an olive branch, while I can find no representation undoubtedly portraying that highly distinctive shrub, the myrtle, the former goes up into Class I. And the most notable of the other candidates in Class II are: first, two other plants in the Blue Bird Panel, the rose and the pea, where it is easy enough to identify the botanic family or even genus but not the species, and one, Evans' 'Anemone', from Zakro in Vol II, p. 472, fig. 279, where the flowers certainly look like those of one of the many-petalled species of *Anemone*, probably the common endemic Cretan white one known as *A. heldreichii*, to which, however the leaves most emphatically do not belong. As for my third class, I cannot put any name to most of the plants in it.

But there are just two points of detail I would like to make. First, I very much doubt whether the peculiar bowls of Vol. I, p. 241 were really inspired by a particular flower, whether a lotus or a water-lily. And second, I cannot help suspecting that the Tulip of Vol. I, p. 606, Pl. 446 is more an Evansian than a Minoan creation.

There, then, is a list of the identifiable plants whose pictures had already come to light at Knossos by the time Evans published his big book.

Since then there have been discoveries at other Minoan sites. Amnisos, for instance, in addition to what in my judgment is by far the best painting of Madonna lilies, may for all I know have disclosed others of plants not represented at Knossos. Thera certainly has. The question is: where did the

Minoans find these plants to paint? It is no easy task to decide what plants could or could not have grown in any particular area some three and a half thousand years ago. Certainly some of my list, notably again the Madonna lily, seem now to be absent from Crete. Having argued that the size of the ancient conduits at Knossos suggests a more plentiful water supply in those days than in these, Sir Arthur Evans writes:

The occurrence of certain species of plants, not now found in the neighbourhood, amongst those depicted on the walls points to the same conclusion that there was a more humid climate in Minoan times.

I am inclined to agree. The progressive clearing of forests on the island would lead not only to a progressively lower rainfall but also to the progressive extinction of a woodland flora. In my view Papyrus is the only plant in the list which could not have grown wild near Knossos in the Minoan era.

When we move on to the treasures of Thera, I must confine myself to a few dry factual statements, basing them on Marinatos' published reports, *Excavations at Thera*. As at Knossos, so at Thera, leafy reed-stems are a common and apparently conventional decorative feature. And other plants already familiar from Knossos recur likewise: the Crocus of the Saffron Gatherer in *Thera* IV, Pl. 8; the Madonna Lily in II, pl. 25, III, Pl. 48, 2 and in numerous plates in *Thera* IV; and, more importantly in view of the remarkable frieze where the plant assumes what Marinatos terms 'supernatural size' (that is, *Thera* IV, Pl. E and F from the 'Ladies' Room'), the sand lily, *Pancratium maritimum*, in its usual stylised guise. At least two other plants here make their first appearance on the scene. First come barley-heads, of which detailed and sensitive representations can be seen in *Thera* II, Pl. 36, 1, and IV, Col. Pl. H, c and Pl. 73. And secondly comes one of the two plants depicted on the bowl of which a photograph can be seen in *Thera* V, Pl. 62, c. The bowl itself evidently interested Marinatos, who describes it as a 'Yellow clay bowl of peculiar

fabric'. The plant, which Marinatos dismissed simply as 'A crocus' I regard as a remarkably faithful picture of one of the three Cretan species of tulip, namely *Tulipa cretica*, and in that case it extends man's knowledge of that particular plant backwards by well over 2 millennia. I would also suggest that the plant accompanying the tulip on the top is a two-headed specimen, by no means unusual, of one of the many colour forms of *Ranunculus asiaticus*.

Three major paintings unearthed at Thera are especially interesting. The first, Plate 8 of *Thera* VI, is a long low frieze depicting the banks of a winding river inhabited by a varied and fascinating fauna and flora. Among the plants portrayed are not only the first truly naturalistic palm-trees, there are also several specimens of two curious plants, both entirely leafless, which seem to be highly stylised versions of the flowering stems of the sand-lily, *Pancratium maritimum*, and of Theocritus's κύπειρος, galingale. We have here in fact an outstanding example of the happy blend of the naturalistic with the stylised. But in the other two paintings, actually both of the same plant, we have Minoan naturalism at its purest and best. One, which justly occupies Colour Plates A to C as well as Plates 121–5 of *Thera* IV, is the magnificent mural from the so-called 'Lilies Room' depicting a continuous multi-coloured cliff, the top and projections of which are at intervals colonised by red-flowered lilies, with here and there swallows gaily flitting above them. And the other, Plate 3 in *Thera* VI, *Colour Plates and Plans* and entitled 'West house, window of room 4 ("bedroom")', shows a more formal but in its own way equally accomplished rendering of the same lily growing this time in a large flower-pot. At one point in the *Historia* and one only, namely VI.6. 3, Theophrastus does mention in passing that some lilies are said to be crimson (πορφυρᾶ); and Thiselton-Dyer identifies them with the scarlet *Lilium chalcedonicum* which occurs only in Greece, rather than with the commoner and more widespread martagon lily, *L. martagon*, which varies in colour from pink to maroon. Of course

Theophrastus' crimson lily is not necessarily the same as the Minoans'. But I prefer an identification with *L. martagon*, partly on grounds of colour but much more because nearly every stem of the Minoan lily bears either 6 or 7 flowers, as in *L. martagon*, whereas wild *L. chalcedonicum* seldom bears more than three. But my dominant feeling is,

in these instances at least wholeheartedly to echo the words quoted earlier from Alice Lindsell:

And even the sceptic, if he will but think how much easier it is to pen the word πολύγναμπτον (polugnampton) than to depict such a leaf on a vase or even a wall, will perhaps forgive these pioneer painters their occasional shortcomings.

LECTURE 4

PRIMITIVE MEDICINE

THE RHIZOTOMISTS AND DRUGGISTS

CRATEVAS AND THE ILLUSTRATION OF PLANTS

THE CODEX VINDOBONENSIS

DIOSCORIDES' HERBAL, ITS NATURE
AND INFLUENCE

As an introduction to the pharmacological tradition in early Greek botany, an unpublished memorandum provided for me by the anthropologist Sir Edmund Leach [1910–1989] on the relation between the 'primitive' and 'scientific' attitudes to medicine is highly relevant:

Anthropologists of late have done a good deal of research into the taxonomic systems of non-literate cultures. Some of the results have been surprising. Botanical and zoological discriminations are quite commonly extremely elaborate and actually yield more taxa than are distinguished by scientific classifications. There is one major difference between folk taxonomies of this kind and scientific taxonomy. A scientist seeks to describe exhaustively the whole of his universe, all species are equally interesting. The folk taxonomist, on the other hand, is mainly interested in things he can see. Many primitive technical processes, eg. those used in the preparation of dye stuffs and of medicines, are often extremely complicated and involve the use of very large numbers of ingredients. While it is very likely that some of the details are functionally redundant, it is very difficult to discover which these are. The native practitioners do not know and research has often shown that the critical common-sense of Europeans in such matters is quite misleading. The success rate of herbalist doctors in primitive societies does not seem to be notably different from that of allegedly scientific doctors in our own system. This is simply because most people will recover in any case from most illnesses, provided they have not been poisoned in the meantime. Most medicines in all kinds of societies operate as placebos. They persuade the patient that the doctor, a man of power, is doing something. Very few medicines can be shown to have automatic consequences of a curative kind, but there are many which produce symptoms, e.g. they reduce pain, cause purgation, change the colour of the urine or the faeces and so on. Present day doctors impress their patients by such devices and folk doctors do the same. A good deal of primitive medical practice is concerned with building up the status of the doctor as a man of power. This is not just hocus pocus. The more the patient believes in his doctor the more likely he is to be cured. The sort of thing mentioned by Theophrastus needs to be understood in these terms. Any medical material which is regarded as potent is ipso facto dangerous, so the preparation and handling of such things will always be subject to safety precautions. The force of the rules is to enhance belief in the potency of the stuff. If you examine the rules which in our own society govern the handling and transport of dangerous chemicals you will find that the level of rationality is almost equally tenuous.

Throughout the entire period of Greek antiquity there seems to have been people whose only job consisted in the digging and preparing of certain roots and, presumably, the gathering of herbs for medicinal purposes. The brief passage in the *Iliad* cited earlier indicates that the 'bitter root', used so effectively to staunch the flow of blood from the wound, was ready to hand when needed. It had presumably been provided by one of these professional root-cutters or ῥιζοτόμοι (rhizotomoi). Theophrastus, in Book IX of the *Historia*, the latter half of which is a curious appendix on the medicinal properties of plants, writes as follows:

Of all the plants used as drugs the one called Elaterion keeps longest, and indeed the older it is the better. At least a certain doctor, who was no boaster nor liar, said that he had some that was 200 years old and still wonderfully effective, which somebody had given him as a present.

a statement which, if neither boastful nor lying, places the preparation of the drug well back into the 6th century. Moreover, the fact that Sophocles wrote a play entitled οἱ ῥιζοτόμοι (hoi rhizotomoi), of which only a very brief fragment remains, is sufficient indication that the profession was familiar in the 5th century as well. And finally the jibes in Greek comedy directed, if not against the ῥιζοτόμοι themselves, then against their associates in the same racket, the druggists or φαρμακοπῶλαι (pharmakopolai), prove clearly enough that the profession was not held in very high esteem.

Unfortunately we know little about these root-cutters beyond what Theophrastus tells us in Book IX. Having described some of their practices and beliefs, he remarks that 'such tales proceed from men who desire to glorify their craft'. None the less the tales thus dismissed throw light on ancient folk-lore. Thus the root-cutters hedged their root-gathering practices with a welter of horrifying superstitions, intended, presumably, to deter the amateur from meddling with their business. Thus, for instance, having described some of the 'statements made by druggists and root-cutters', Theophrastus continues, in *H.P.* IX.8. 6, as follows:

On the other hand the following ideas may be considered far-fetched and irrelevant; for instance, they say that peony should be dug up at night, for, if a man does it in the day-time and is observed by a woodpecker while he is gathering the fruit, he risks the loss of his eyesight, and if he is cutting the root at the time, he gets *prolapsus ani* ... and other reasons for caution are also given. That one should be bidden to pray while cutting is not perhaps unreasonable, but the additions to this injunction are absurd ... Thus it is said that one should draw three circles round mandrake with a sword, and cut it with one's face towards the west; and at the cutting of the second piece one should dance round the plant and say as many things as possible about the mysteries of love ...

and so on and so on. They employed also a more familiar method of 'glorifying their own crafts', that of extolling their beneficial effects. The root-cutters and druggists together evidently spared no pains to commend their wares to a doubtless credulous clientèle, including, apparently, Theophrastus himself. Listen, for example, to the string of ailments, in man and beast alike, which he tells us at *H.P.* IX.9. 2 are cured by the single plant appropriately named πάνακες (panakes) or all-heal:

Various parts of all-heal are also useful, and not all for the same purposes. The fruit is used in cases of miscarriage and also for sprains and such-like troubles; also for the ears and to strengthen the voice. The root is used in child-birth, for diseases of women, and for flatulence in beasts of burden. It is also useful in making the iris-perfume because of its fragrance.

Even modern pharmaceutical firms would be hard pressed to outdo that list of multifarious uses for one and the same drug.

Yet even among the root-cutters there would seem to have been a few notable individuals with a more scientific approach. Theophrastus, once again in Book IX, tells us a little about some of these individuals. Thrasyas of Mantinea, for example, would seem to have some claim to be called a genuinely empirical scientist. Not only, according to Theophrastus, did he discover a vegetable poison, consisting of the juices of hemlock, poppy and other plants, which produces an easy and painless death, but he also discovered that familiarity with certain poisons produces immunity, For, as Theophrastus writes with due acknowledgement at *H.P.* IX.17. 2.

When the constitution has accepted and prevailed over them, they cease to be poisons, as Thrasyas also remarked; for he said that the same thing was a poison to one and not to another.

And similarly a certain Eudemus of Chios had so immunised himself against the emetic effects of hellebore that, again in the words of Theophrastus,

On one occasion he said that in a single day he took 22 draughts in the market place as he sat at his stall, and did not leave the place till it was evening when he went home, had a bath, and dined in the usual way without being sick.

This practical experiment at least shows scientific curiosity allied to commendable fortitude.

The most important contribution to early Greek pharmacology is that of the Hippocratic Corpus. This as a whole contains the names of some 250 different plants, a marked advance on any earlier literature, but presumably because these names were already familiar in medical circles, the authors seldom if ever bother to describe the plants they name. Perhaps the passage in the whole Corpus most relevant to our present topic is in the second book on *Regimen*, Chapters

54 and 55. It gives a straightforward account of the digestive and other medical properties of no less than 47 vegetables or herbs and 17 sorts of fruit. I can deal equally concisely with the poet Nicander of Colophon, who probably flourished around the middle of the second century B.C. In his two surviving poems Nicander mentions no fewer than 125 different plants, some 30 of them for the first time in extant literature, but says nothing of the slightest value about any of them.

Much more important is Cratevas, physician to King Mithridates VI Eupator and the author of one of the most influential of all early herbals. Unfortunately his illustrated herbal has perished as a whole like all its predecessors, which number at least three and include an equally influential one in the ῥιζοτομικόν (Rhizotomikon) of the Sicilian doctor Diocles. But Max Wellmann, editor of the authoritative text of Dioscorides, has convincingly shown that a number of excerpts from it have survived in the form of interpolations into an early manuscript of Dioscorides called the *Codex Aniciae Julianae nunc Vindobonensis* or, more simply, the Vienna Codex; Charles Singer has argued that a number of illustrations in that remarkable manuscript are actually copies of original drawings by Cratevas.

From the remarkably high repute that the work of Cratevas enjoyed in ancient times, clearly he raised the art to an unprecedented height.

The *Codex Vindobonensis* dates from about 512 A.D., when it was prepared and given as a wedding present to a certain Juliana Anicia, daughter of Anicius Olybrius, Emperor of the West. As a text of Dioscorides it is unreliable, since it certainly contains numerous interpolations from a variety of other sources. Its great glory lies partly in its early date, partly in the very beautiful capitals in which it is transcribed, but chiefly in the great number of its large illustrations. Those illustrations, like the text, are a mixed batch. A few appear to be nothing more than stiff and stylised representations of wholly fictitious plants. The epitome of these is of course Mandragoras or mandrake which is portrayed as the figure of a man with spirally twisted arms, one foot apparently a hoof and the other a tail-fin, and a bouquet of leaves and berries sprouting from the top of his head.

Others, however, such as that of *Euphorbia cyparissias* (C.V. f. 349 recto), the cypress spurge, or of the garden onion, *Allium cepa* (C.V. f. 185 verso), are astonishingly lifelike: in many cases there is no difficulty in identifying, if not the precise species, at any rate the genus to which it belongs.

None of these drawings originates from Dioscorides himself; and indeed, though each of these is intended to accompany a particular description by Dioscorides, there can be little doubt that the plant drawn is in some cases different from the plant described. The illustrations are all done in some kind of colour wash, and many of them reveal, besides a notable accuracy of botanical detail, a surprising grasp of the principles of shading. The Vienna Codex has been twice reproduced in facsimile, in black and white in 1906, in colour in 1970. The best of the illustrations, which date at the latest from 512 A.D., were for about a thousand years far superior to anything else produced.

If, as is certainly possible but cannot be conclusively proved, the best of them all are indeed copied from Cratevas, then their interest is still further enhanced by the fact that they date instead from about 75 B.C. Thus it might be plausibly claimed that Cratevas founded the tradition of lifelike plant illustration which gave rise not only to the best drawings in the Vienna Codex but also to the numberless plant drawings of later times.

Dioscorides was a botanist only incidentally; as an army doctor he was naturally interested in plants from a medical or pharmacological not from a botanical standpoint; and accordingly his treatise is rightly entitled περὶ ὕλης ἰατρικῆς or *De materia medica*, not περὶ φυτῶν or *De plantis*. And secondly, though he is indisputably great, that is largely because he has had greatness thrust upon him: as Greene emphasized, he has exercised right down to the present day a greater influence than any other botanical writer of all time; but the extent to which he deserved his reputation is an altogether different question.

In the course of the five books of his herbal Dioscorides mentions a total of over 500 plants, almost all of them dealt with individually, in separate paragraphs or short chapters headed by the plant's name. The accounts are very variable, both in length and in scope. Here is an example of the briefest kind of treatment:

Calamagrostis is larger in all its parts than Agrostis. When eaten by domestic animals it kills them, especially that which grows by the roadsides in Babylon.

That is chapter 30 of Book IV.

First, instead of introducing us, as later examples will, to a welter of unfamiliar and unidentifiable plants, it very obligingly, by taking on ἄγρωστις εἰλιτενής (or *Agrostis stolonifera*) as its standard of comparison, re-introduces us to a plant already met on the fringe of Hylas' pool. And second, and more important, it contrives, for all its brevity, to include all the elements that go to make up any one of Dioscorides' descriptions. First comes the name – *Calamagrostis*; secondly a description of the plant –'larger in all its parts than *Agrostis*'; thirdly, an account of its alleged medicinal or pharmacological properties – 'When eaten by domestic animals it kills them'; fourthly the type of habitat it prefers – 'by road-sides'; and finally its geographical locality – 'in Babylon'. Of these five elements, the name of course invariably occurs, likewise the account of its medicinal properties; and also some description of the appearance of the plant is nearly always included. But unfortunately the type of habitat it frequents is comparatively seldom mentioned, and even less regularly or fully its geographical distribution.

A surprisingly high proportion of the names, as with Theophrastus, so again with Dioscorides, still remain in universal use as the names of modern botanical genera, e.g. *Calamagrostis* and *Agrostis*. Furthermore, though the Dioscoridean one-word names, again like the Theophrastan, suffice in a genus of only one species, they still need the addition of a specific epithet before they can precisely designate one kind of plant and one only in a genus containing several kinds. Accordingly there

are occasional sections in Dioscorides where the need to distinguish kinds within a genus has resulted in two-word names virtually indistinguishable from Linnaean binomials. Thus in Book IV, chapters 63 to 65, he not only distinguishes between different species of poppy with precision sufficient for reasonably confident identifications but attaches to each an apparently conventional and accepted two-word name, such as μήκων ῥοιάς or μήκων κερατῖτις (mekon keratitis). However in chapter 66 a plant he calls by the comparable name of μήκων ἀφρώδης (mekon aphrodes) is certainly not a poppy at all. The fact remains that Dioscorides, like his contemporary Pliny, has come nearer to anticipating the Linnaean binomial system as a standard shorthand method of indicating specific distinctions than Theophrastus ever did, despite the descriptive epithets that he applied, for example, to particular plants which collectively he called κάλαμος (kalamos) or even κρόκος (krokos).

Dioscorides' plant descriptions are of widely varying value. A few are so brief that they are insufficient to identify the plant. But the majority describe, sometimes in considerable detail and with a commendable grasp of the essential, the flower and seed, the stalk and leaves, and of course the root. Dioscorides, like Theophrastus before him, suffers from the lack of a technical vocabulary; and so, again like Theophrastus, he repeatedly describes a plant by comparing and contrasting it with another. But unfortunately, unlike Theophrastus, he did not choose a few familiar and easily identifiable plants as his regular standards of comparison but simply compared the plant he was attempting to describe with any other plant which struck him as in any respect similar. The result is that, for a particular plant, Dioscorides' description of some vital part all too often simply compares it with the corresponding part of another plant; that other in turn is contrasted with a third, and so on until, in the end, the account of the plant in the chain may refer back, by way of comparison or contrast, to the very first plant of them all. As an example of the kind of description that may easily deter further investigation, here are the opening sentences of the account, in Book III, chapter 7, of the plant called κενταύρειον τὸ λεπτὸν ἢ μικρόν (kentaureion to lepton e mikron):

It is a plant like Hypericum or Origanum, with a square stalk more than a span long, purplish-red flowers like those of Lychnis, and small, rather long leaves like those of Peganon.

If you happen to know what *Hypericum, Origanum, Lychnis* and *Peganon* are, then well and good. Otherwise beware. But occasionally the characteristics of a plant are such that even a non-technical vocabulary is adequate to describe them; then Dioscorides' accounts usually prove to be both accurate and graphic, for example his description, in chapter 178 of Book II, of the plant which he calls *Anagallis*:

There are 2 kinds of Anagallis, differing in the flower. The kind with a blue flower is called the female, that with the scarlet flower the male. They are little bushy plants spreading on the ground, with small roundish leaves, like those of Helxine, on 4-cornered stalks, and with spherical fruit.

Here the two colour variants, the spreading habit, the angled stem and spherical fruit point unmistakably to the genus still called *Anagallis* and to the species, *A. arvensis*, the scarlet pimpernel, and *A. foemina*, the blue pimpernel. Moreover the two coloured illustrations in the *Codex Vindobonensis* ff. 39 verso, 40 verso are not only particularly good in themselves but also fit the description to perfection. The pity is that there are not more descriptions with the same grasp of essential features and the same concise clarity of language.

Dioscorides' notes about the type of habitat a plant prefers, which are always, when they occur at all, as brief as they could be, none the less leave little of importance to be added, and seem to be based on accurate field observation. The most he ever tells us is something like 'It flowers in the springs in vineyards and cultivated ground' or 'It loves a rich soil open to the sun, but grows also in

woods and on hills'. These brief notes call for comment. Dioscorides does not claim to be the earliest Greek author to have included such information in his writings: Theophrastus certainly recorded occasional observations of this sort, and presumably the other and earlier herbalists whose works have perished did the same.

Dioscorides, once again reflecting the influence of Theophrastus, had certainly some notion of the geographical range of plants. In the earlier part of his herbal in particular he usually refers briefly to the countries or districts in which a plant occurs. These geographical references raise matters of some interest.

Dioscorides was evidently fully aware that some plants are peculiarly local in their distribution. For instance, he writes of the balsam tree that it is found only 'in a certain valley in Judaea'. Moreover, he had apparently covered a surprisingly wide range of territory in his quest for medicinal plants. Every country is mentioned from Spain in the West, where he tells us, for example, that a plant called 'Meon' grows in abundance, to India in the East, where plant after plant is said to occur. His references to India may be based on hearsay but an occasional passage, such as that on nard in Book III chapter 7, suggests that he might have visited India himself. Discussing Indian nard he writes that

One kind is called Gangitis, from a certain river called Ganges that flows by the mountain. It grows by this river and is weaker and taller [than the Syrian kind] owing to its inhabiting watery places. But that which grows further up the hill...

and so on. Many commercial Greeks had settled in India by the first century A.D. and, although Dioscorides seems to have spent part of his life as a medical man in the armies of Nero, which could account for much of his globe-trotting, he would almost certainly have made his 'Passage to India' for private or commercial rather than from military purposes.

The main content of the herbal of Dioscorides consists of accounts of the medicinal properties of plants. Years ago I said that 'mixed up among the welter of magical mumbo-jumbo there is an occasional observation that not only happens to be true but also points unmistakably to the rudiments of empirical science'. On this matter, however, Professor F.W. Fairbairn of the School of Pharmacy, University of London, wrote to me that Dioscorides' work is 'far from being full of "mumbo-jumbo"' and that 'I am quite impressed with his careful observations, and interesting accounts of the use of these remedies. For instance, his monograph on Opium (Meconium) is very sound even in the light of modern research' and 'Similarly, his remarks on Liquorice are, in some ways, more up-to-date than the information I received as a student'.

In view of the generally encouraging tone of Professor Fairbairn's letter, I got in touch with his former student, now Principal Lecturer in Pharmacognosy at the School of Pharmacy and Biology at Sunderland, Dr. Betty P. Jackson, and I have received from her much valuable information, some of it given below.

The first and perhaps the most significant fact to have so far emerged is the longevity of the herb-lore tradition, both before and after the time of Dioscorides. Having devoted the first book and a half to a miscellany of medical recipes ranging from oils and ointments, through living creatures and dairy produce, to cereals, Dioscorides thereafter confines his attention for the next two and a half books to strictly herbal remedies. In the concluding 85 chapters of Book II, he mentions in all something under a hundred different plants. Of this total, Dr. Jackson assures me, over half (or, to be precise, at least 53) still find a place in the European herbalists' pharmacopaeia, and as many as 35 of them actually in British homoeopathic or 'folk' medicine. And moreover she adds: 'There is a much wider use of herbal medicines in other European countries than there is in Britain and it is probable that most of those which I have included are in common use, in parts of Europe, as orthodox remedies'.

It must suffice here merely to list a few of the most notable, in the order in which Dioscorides discussed them.

In Book I there is Cardamom in chapter 6, Cassia in 13; the most familiar of several in Book II is σκίλλα (skilla) or squill of ch. 171; Book III has rhubarb in ch. 2, aloes in ch. 22; and most important of all for my present purposes, Book IV, ch. 68 contains an unusually long account of *Hyoscyamus*.

Another plant of especial note is *Mandragora* or mandrake. After describing how a decoction is made by boiling the plant's root in wine, Dioscorides first tells us that some nameless practitioners use it, in his own words,

on those suffering from insomnia or acute pain or those in whom, when undergoing an operation or cauterisation, they wish to induce anaesthesia.

He later adds, again in his own words, that a man will sleep, feeling nothing whatever, for up to 3 or 4 hours after the dose is given him, and doctors use it when they are going to operate or cauterise.

There can be no shadow of doubt that, some 1800 years before the generally accepted date of the discovery of anaesthetics, at least one anaesthetic, presumably hyoscine or, more popularly, 'twilight sleep', was already in apparently regular use. For that piece of information alone, if for nothing else, Dioscorides has surely earned his immortality.

Regarding the effective substances in *Mandragora* and other plants of the same botanical family, the Solanaceae, Dr. Jackson wrote:

First, to answer your question about Mandragora. So far as I know, it has no use in modern medicine although I believe it is still occasionally gathered and used in folk medicine. It contains alkaloids similar to those found in Belladonna (that is, *Atropa belladonna*, the true deadly nightshade) and it is difficult to understand why it was once reputed to act as an anaesthetic. The alkaloids *do* include hyoscine, which has sedative properties, but the amount present is too small to have much effect. I have noticed that some of the old recipes containing Mandragora also contain Hyoscyamus, which is a richer source of hyoscine, and I have often wondered if, perhaps, it was the Hyoscyamus which was responsible for the anaesthetic action. Anyway, to return to your question, Hyoscine is extracted from various plants of the Solanaceae (particularly Hyoscyamus and Belladonna, but *not* Mandragora), and is occasionally used as a mild hypnotic.

If to this we add Dioscorides' statement that Hyoscyamus 'is effective when mixed with other pain-killing poultices', I am convinced that she has found the right answer. The doctors cited by Dioscorides employed a mixture of *Mandragora* and *Hyoscyamus*, and possibly also other plants such as the opium poppy, *Papaver somniferum*, and Dioscorides, or else his sources of information, then attributed the hypnotic and anaesthetic effect to the wrong ingredient in the mixture. I tentatively suggest that we witness here a stage in the gradual emergence of scientific from primitive medicine.

Like other compilers of standard works, Dioscorides obviously took much information from his herbalist or botanical predecessors, whose works are now in the main lost. Thus, irrespective of Max Wellmann's convincing demonstration of the debt that Dioscorides owed to Cratevas, throughout the pages of the *De materia medica* are many obvious echoes from the *Historia plantarum* of Theophrastus.

A careful reading and comparison of the two texts establishes beyond any question that they are in one way or the other interdependent. Out of numerous examples I have chosen, simply for its brevity, that of 'the so-called male spurge', ὁ ἄρρην καλούμενος τιθύμαλλα. The Theophrastan or Pseudo-Theophrastan description of it, in IX.1. 8, runs to a mere four lines, but virtually every word or phrase of it is echoed, or at least paraphrased, in the much longer account in Dioscorides IV.164.

Even though Dioscorides freely used earlier works, if greatness is to be correlated with subsequent influence, then his greatness is indisputable. Numberless available instances prove this. Thus when, in 1534, a chair of botany was first instituted at the University of Bologna, its first holder, Luca Ghini, was described in the *Herbal* of his student William Turner, the greatest pioneer among English naturalists, as 'Lucas Gynus the reader of Dioscorides in Bonony my maister'.

A much later example of Dioscorides' long lasting influence will be found in an article entitled 'A botanist on the Holy Mountain' in *Blackwood's Magazine* by Sir Arthur W. Hill, which describes his visit in 1934, together with two other Kew botanists, to Mount Athos, the Holy Mountain of northern Greece:

A Botanist on the Holy Mountain … is no new thing; for there is at Karyés "The Botanist" par excellence, the Herbalist Monk, who wanders over the peninsula collecting plants of real and supposed medicinal value – a truly remarkable man with a considerable knowledge of plants and their properties. He quickly learnt of our visit and made the six hours' journey across the peninsula to call on us, no doubt to see whom it might be who was trespassing on his preserves. When he found we were collecting plants most of which he considered worthless, his estimation of us, I fear, considerably diminished. It was of interest to see him at work. Sometimes he travelled on foot, and, like the other monks, covered the ground with astonishing rapidity, while sometimes for longer journeys he rode a mule. He was, of course, fully gowned in his black cassock with his black cylindrical hat, and on his back he carried a large and bulky bag. This contained his 'Flora', which was no less than four manuscript folio volumes of Dioscorides, copied possibly by his own hand. A somewhat voluminous work for identifying one's plants in the field.

When he came to us he was busy collecting Henbane (*Hyoscyamus*) for medicinal purposes. He presented one of us with a piece of wild liquorice root to chew; the sickly sweet taste lasted for over an hour and the experiment was not repeated. On being asked the name of a plant unfamiliar to us he at once opened his bag and produced his Dioscorides, and hastily turning over the pages of the bulky volumes pointed out his identification. This was quite a remarkable feat considering the nature of the work and the condition of the manuscript.

Well, the purport of that passage, the peaceful coexistence, right down into the present century, of primitive and scientific botany and medicine, is plain for all to see. It provides an appropriate ending for these lectures on the plants and plant lore of Ancient Greece.

POSTSCRIPT: AMATEURS OF ANCIENT BOTANY

NICHOLAS JARDINE

It is necessary to any originality to have the courage to be an amateur

(*Wallace Stevens*)

At the time I wrote for *John Raven by his Friends* about John's Gray Lectures, I knew little of the background to his interest in ancient botany. Since then, guided by William Stearn's masterly introduction to the published version, I have looked at some of the work of other scholars on plants in ancient literature. In addition, I have had the opportunity to read in manuscript a delightful informal talk that John gave in 1971, and to go through the notebooks and documents relating to Greek botany that John had collected. Amongst these papers of John's is a correspondence between his former tutor, the Trinity classicist Andrew Gow and Miss Alice Lindsell, who had been a student at Newnham. With the help of Phyllis Hetzel, Deborah Hodder, and Marina Frasca-Spada, Newnhamites all, and Sophie H. Badham, archivist of Royal Holloway, University of London, I have been able to gather a little information about Miss Lindsell's life and works. In the light of this, I offer some further reflections on John's approach to ancient botany.

In the Gray Lectures John lambasted Sir William Turner Thiselton-Dyer, arch-conservative successor to Joseph Dalton Hooker as Director of the Royal Botanic Gardens at Kew, author of the entries for plant names in Liddell and Scott's *Greek-English Lexicon* and of the article 'Flora' in Whibley's *Companion to Greek Studies*. William Stearn suggests that John's treatment of Sir William was not altogether fair; and he is mildly critical of John for having failed to take account of the work of other scholars – mainly German – on ancient plant names. Having looked at Thiselton-Dyer's 'Flora' as well as his articles in *Classical Philology,* I endorse Stearn's charge of unfairness. Indeed, I conjecture that had John read the ponderously learned German tomes Stearn cites he would have judged them no less harshly and unfairly. John's animus against Thiselton-Dyer and his ilk was, I think, motivated not just, as

Stearn maintains, by their dogmatism, but also by their *method*. The "classicist" approach exemplified by Thiselton-Dyer was a literary and philological one, seeking understanding of ancient plant names through a meticulous compilation of their symbolic, religious, medical and culinary contexts. To be fair – as John was inclined not to be – in Thiselton-Dyer, as in Senn, Möbius, and others cited by Stearn, note is also taken of the habits and distributions of plants; but the focus remains literary and scholarly rather than botanical or historical. To this John objected with his characteristic *faux-naif* common sense that if we are to understand a passage of ancient literature dealing with plants we need first to find out precisely which plants are being referred to and precisely what was the nature of the author's interest in them.

In the third, and in my view finest, of his Gray Lectures, John heaped praise on Miss Alice Lindsell's pioneering work on Theocritus' botany. Amongst his papers are to be found substantial manuscript remains of Miss Lindsell's (now given by Faith Raven to Newnham College Library): a seven-volume glossary of plant names in ancient Greek literature; a marvellous book of pencil and wash portrayals of native Greek plants dating from 1931; a volume of tracings of plant motifs on Cycladic and Cretan pottery; an article, here published, but rejected by *Greece and Rome* in 1937, demolishing Thiselton-Dyer's identification of κρόκος in the *Companion to Greek Studies*; notes and maps concerning the topography of Cos and Samos; and, most revealingly of all, her correspondence with Andrew Gow, Fellow and Tutor of Trinity College and the leading Theocritus scholar of his generation. It seems that these materials came into Gow's hands at the time of Miss Lindsell's death in 1948 and that he in turn passed them on to John. They tell us a lot about the origins and motivations of John's work on classical botany.

Miss Lindsell had read classics at Newnham, 1900–1904, and was briefly Secretary to the Principal of Newnham and Secretary of the College Garden Committee (not a College librarian, as I wrongly stated in my piece in *John Raven by His Friends*). From 1919 to 1939 she was warden of Bedford College House, the first college of higher education for women in Britain (in 1985 merged with Royal Holloway College). Immediately on publication of her "Was Theocritus a botanist?" in *Greece and Rome* (1937, and here pp. 63–75), Miss Lindsell received a letter of cautious approval from the reserved and severe Gow. And in the preface to his Theocritus edition we find the following appreciation of her work.

A little light would seem to be thrown on the poet's early life by Miss Alice Lindsell's study of his botany. Miss Lindsell pointed out that there are references to far more plants and trees in the Idylls, most of them in the bucolic Idylls, than in the whole of Homer, and that Theocritus is remarkably accurate both as to the habit and to the habitat of those he mentions. This knowledge and interest must ultimately derive from Theophrastus, the father of the science, who lived into the third century, and they are likely to have been acquired in Cos, where the students of the famous medical school would be specially interested in the subject. And certainly it seems probable that in the first part of the third century such knowledge, whether acquired in Cos or not, would have been more easily come by in the East than in Sicily. Further Miss Lindsell noticed that there are marked differences between the flora of Greek lands and that of Sicily, and that Theocritus' landscapes are characteristically Greek and not Sicilian. She concluded, therefore, that he left Sicily at an early age …

These positive appraisals are more remarkable than they may at first sight appear. In his dryly titled "The methods of Theocritus and some problems in his poems" (*Classical Quarterly*, 1930), Gow had emphasised the artificiality of the Idylls and had adduced their many apparent inconsistencies as evidences of Theocritus' 'indifference to detail'. Yet here was Miss Lindsell insisting on Theocritus' meticulous observations of plants in their local settings, and claiming (as Gow put it) that 'no detail in Theocritus is to be condemned'.

Over the next three years Gow and Lindsell exchanged letters. Gow encouraged Miss Lindsell to undertake a more substantial publication, perhaps even a book on plants in ancient literature; and her seven-volume glossary suggests that she may indeed have planned such a work. But the main topic of the exchange was Theocritus' Seventh Idyll, "The harvest festival". There Simichidas, the narrator, accompanied by two friends goes from town to take part in a harvest festival to Demeter, engaging in a song contest with the goatherd Lycidas encountered on the way. What was their route, and at what time of year? Miss Lindsell visited Cos and provided Gow with notes on Coan topography and agriculture. In an article in *Classical Quarterly* for 1940 Gow made use of this information, but persisted in finding carelessness in Theocritus juxtaposition of the barley harvest – April, in present-day Cos, as Miss Lindsell had told him – with ripe pears, apples and sloes. Miss Lindsell pointed out to him that the ancients had customarily laid the ears of barley to ripen on the threshing floor. Gow conceded defeat:

Thank you for your letter. The date is unquestionably the winnowing which I had assumed to follow immediately on the harvest. But I agree that this was a mistake. Hesiod (W.D.598) winnows about the first week in July, but I see that the Geoponica contemplate its going on in August. I will look into this. In the meantime can you throw any light on the poppies (157): when would they be flowering? Three months seems a long time to leave the stuff unwinnowed, but I dare say it is all right: I will perhaps print a correction when I have gone into the evidence.

He did publish the correction, in a later number of the same volume of *Classical Quarterly*.

It is my impression that Miss Lindsell persuaded Gow of far more than the seasonal consistency of the Seventh Idyll. As far as I can tell, Gow never explicitly recanted his earlier claims about Theocritus' indifference to detail. But in his edition and commentary of 1950, Theocritus appears, for all the artifice and artificiality of his herdsmen and their songs, as a close and careful observer of the natural world, as the poet whom Wordsworth had admired and emulated because his genius was a *genius loci*.

It is no wonder that John paid such generous tribute to Miss Lindsell's work. For whilst he disagreed on botanical and ecological grounds with certain of her conclusions, he regarded her method as admirable. The questions she asked of his favorite poet, Theocritus – which plants was he talking about? where? and why? – were precisely the questions he asked of all the authors discussed in his Gray Lectures.

Whilst at Trinity John himself had started work on a glossary of ancient Greek plant names, and in a letter of 1967 he talks of his plans to publish something comparable to D'Arcy Thompson's great glossaries of Greek birds and fishes. However, John's view of his task became steadily more ambitious, both botanically and historically. With successive visits to Greece he developed ever more extensive concerns with the taxonomy, ecology, and pharmacology of Greek plants. These interests are to the fore in his splendid paper for the Oxford Alpine Garden Society. And he showed an ever livelier appreciation of the variety of ancient Greek involvements with plants: medical, culinary, aesthetic, and philosophical – though he remained oddly reticent about their ceremonial and religious uses. This is the focus of another fine talk, to the Swan Hellenic Cruise Society. Alas, the task was now impossibly huge.

It is sad that no book completed the enterprise initiated by Miss Lindsell, fostered by Gow and pursued with such verve by John. But it would be wrong to judge it a failure. Miss Lindsell's paper on Theocritus' botany is a minor classic. Her glossary of plant names, now housed in Newnham College Library, will be an invaluable resource for future students of ancient botany. Most importantly, Miss Lindsell's papers and John's Gray Lectures are exemplary in their approach, in their combination of botanical and historical common sense with a passionate curiosity about plants, places and people.

A Note on Greek Crocus

Alice Lindsell
(1937)

In his magnificent contribution 'Flora' to *A Companion to Greek Studies* Sir William Thiselton-Dyer, like Homer, nodded. He nodded over the crocus. His note is this: 'Crocus, κρόκος: the Greeks included under the name the golden-flowered species: that of Mt Ida, which 'brake like fire' (Tennyson) is *C. gargaricus*; the κ. χρυσαυγής in Soph. *O.C.* is *C. Olivieri* or *C. aureus*; Eur. *Ion* 890 refers to *C. chrysanthus*, a mountain species; see also Saffron.'[1] On seeing also saffron I find: 'Saffron, κρόκος, *Crocus sativus*:[2] the flowers are pale purple, the dye-stuff consists in the orange-coloured styles and stigmas.'[3]

Thiselton-Dyer's distinction between the saffron crocus, *Crocus sativus*, and the other crocuses of Greece implies a similar distinction between them in Greek literature. This in a sense exists. There is on the one hand the trade or business crocus which supplied the dye: there is on the other hand what I will call the poetical crocus; that is, either crocus species other than the saffron, or the saffron crocus in a poetical aspect, with its dye qualities ignored or at least subsidiary.

In deference to its double role, I will begin with *Crocus sativus*. It grows all over the foothills of the Attic mountains and is still called ζαφρονά or ζαφορά, as distinct from other crocuses, which are κατσές. As to its appearance, I at once join issue with Thiselton-Dyer, for in describing this crocus as pale purple he does it less than justice, as also does its portrait in S. C. Atchley's *Wild Flowers of Attica*.[4] The first time I found it, I felt as much excited as if I had seen a parrot in an English wood.

It was more kindly represented 4,000 years ago by a Minoan painter in the frieze of the Saffron Gatherers from the early palace of Knossos, though its colour, as always in Minoan painting, is fanciful.[5] The actual colour is what would be described in nurserymen's catalogues as rich purple, streaked with deep violet,[6] and the styles and stigmas, scarlet rather than orange, loll out of the flower like the tongue of a thirsty dog from its mouth. The flower is large and flamboyant: it is the only Greek crocus which I should describe as showy; it is, in addition, the only one which is scented. This is noticed by Theophrastus, who distinguishes it by its scent from *Crocus cancellatus*, the common white crocus of Greece, as from the safflower:

καθάπερ οὐδὲ ὁ κρόκος οὔτε ὁ εὔοσμος οὔθ' ὁ λευκὸς οὐθ' ὁ ἀκανθώδης· οὗτοι δὲ ἄοσμοι.[7]

In literature the business crocus is responsible for the fairly frequent epithets, κροκόπεπλος. It is mentioned in poetry by, for instance, Chaeremon:

κρόκον θ' ὃς ἡλιώδες εἰς ὑφάσματα, πέπλων σκιᾶς εἴδωλον ἐξωμόργνυτο.[8]

In prose, it is mentioned several times by Strabo: e.g. 'Sicily', he says, 'is superior to Italy

σίτῳ δὲ καὶ μέλιτι καὶ κρόκῳ καὶ ἄλλοις τισί.[9]

So much for *Crocus sativus* in its business aspect. Before I leave it, I give two quotations which mark the transition from the purely business to the purely poetical aspect: the haunting

---

1 *Op. cit.*, p. 57.
2 This crocus has been heavily renamed *Crocus cartwrightianus*, but I have kept to the older, simpler name.
3 *Op. cit.*, p. 66.
4 (Oxford, 1938), Pl. XX.

5 A. J. Evans, *The Palace of Minos at Knossos*, I (London, 1921), Pl. IV.
6 Paler forms exist: I have even found white specimens.
7 VII.7.4; cp., Diosc. I.26: ἐπακτικὸς ἐν τῇ ὀσμῇ.
8 *Trag. frag.* 14 (Nauck).
9 VI.2.7.

I. CROCUS SATIVUS.

κρόκου βαφὰς δ' εἰς πέδον χέουσα

of Aeschylus[10], and Moschus'

αἳ δ' αὖτε ξανθοὶ ο κρόκου θυόεσσαν ἔθειραν δρέπτον ἐριδμαίνουσαι.[11]

The adjective ξανθός has here been transferred from the stigmas to the flower: this, unless the lines are to be taken as sheer poetry, must be the explanation, for, as I hope to show later, no yellow-*petalled* crocus fits the case.

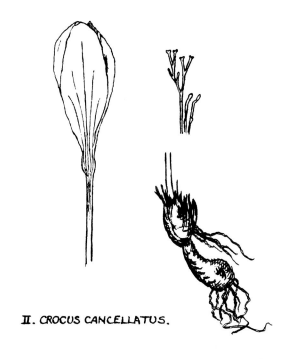

II. CROCUS CANCELLATUS.

The purely poetical crocus is a more complex affair. To it, so far as I have collected them, the following epithets are applied:

Smell: εὔοδμος; εὐώδης; ἡδύς; γλυκύς?

General: ἀγανός; γλυκύς?

Colour: ξανθός; χρυσαυγής; χρυσανταυγής; χρυσανθής.

10 *Ag.* 239.
11 II. 68.

SMELL. As *Crocus sativus* is the one scented crocus it is obvious that the first two epithets, εὔοδμος and εὐώδης, can apply only to it. The same is probably true of the third, ἡδύς, for though ἡδύς can mean 'sweet' in both the English senses of fragrant and charming, the fragrant meaning is commoner. *Crocus sativus* will in any case be the εὔοδμος κρόκος of Orpheus: the εὐώδης κρόκος which scents the tomb of Lais:[12] and the χείματι κρόκος ἡδύς of Callimachus.[13] As to γλυκύς, it has the double meaning of ἡδύς, but in its case the meaning 'fragrant' seems the rarer: I incline, therefore, to remove it from the 'smell' category, and to leave it in the general. Just before I pass to this, there is one more part for my hard-worked *Crocus sativus* to play: Theophrastus classes it among coronary flowers,[14] which is just where one would expect to find it, for in addition to its qualifications of size, colour and scent, it has this further unique charm, that its flowers do not merely open to the sun and then close again at dusk, but once open they remain open, except in very cold weather, day and night until they fade.[15] *Crocus sativus* will then be the κρόκος εἴαρι μύων of Nicander,[16] where it is one of a coronary list, and will have an additional claim on the 'sweet' crocus of the *Anthology*, which has already been allotted to it on the score of scent: πλέξω καὶ κρόκον ἡδύν.[17]

GENERAL. Γλυκύς I have dealt with above. Ἀγανός is 'giving pleasure' or 'giving no pain'. Such an epithet cannot apply to the lusty *Crocus sativus*,[18] nor, as I hope to prove shortly, to any yellow crocus. We need a new peg on which to hang it. Why not the *Crocus cancellatus* mentioned above? It is vouched for by Theophrastus: it is the

12 *Anth.*VII. 218.
13 Hymn II.83.
14 VI.6.10.
15 See Atchley, *Flowers of Attica*, 'Crocus cartwrightianus'.
16 Frag. 74.56.
17 Meleager, *Anth.*, V.147.3.
18 Theoph.VI.6.10: Τὸ ὅλον εὔζωον.

commonest of the crocuses today in Greece: though large and white, or sometimes pale mauve, it is flimsy in texture, and looks as if it were made of tissue paper, which detracts from its personal appearance, so that a negative epithet such as ἀγανός is not misplaced; it is by a long way the earliest crocus to bloom, appearing immediately after the September rains, so γλυκύς may well express the pleasure felt at the sight of it. Let me assume, then, that *Crocus cancellatus* is the ἀγανὸς κρόκος of the Hymn to Demeter, and the γλυκὸς Ἡρίννης κρόκος of the *Anthology*.[19] There is at least nothing against the attribution.

COLOUR. I can now turn to yellow crocuses, to my three golden epithets, and to Thiselton-Dyer. Each of the epithets, so far as I know, occurs exactly once in literature in connection with a crocus.

First χρυσαυγής: Sophocles, in the famous description of Colonus:

θάλλει δ' οὐρανίας ὑπ' ἄχνας
ὁ καλλίβοτρυς κατ' ἦμαρ αἰεὶ
νάρκισσος, μεγάλαιν θεαῖν
ἀρχαῖον στεφάνωμ', ὅ τε
χρυσαυγὴς κρόκος.[20]

'The κ. χρυσαυγής', said Thiselton-Dyer, 'in Soph. *O. C.* is *C. Olivieri* or *C. aureus*'.[21] I wonder. *Crocus aureus* is small, and though in colour it is a marvellous orange, it is only as a specimen in the hand that one observes its beauty: it makes no show growing. I have another objection to it here. Sophocles, it is, I believe, agreed, is giving in his chorus no fancy picture of Colonus, but describing it as he knew it. It is not then overponderous to believe that he had actually seen both narcissi, and what he took to be yellow crocuses growing in it. We know where Colonus was: could these flowers have grown there? The narcissus almost certainly did. It must be

Narcissus tazetta, the common Greek narcissus. It does not actually grow in Colonus today, because Colonus is swallowed up in the modern town, but it is still to be found to the north of Athens, in the plain, so soon as building stops, and shade and water begin, and Colonus had both. *Crocus aureus*, on the other hand, is not a plant of the plain. 'In montosis', says, Halácsy: 'Attica: mt. Parnes, Cithareon'.[22] I have myself found it only some way up Parnes. It could never have grown in low-lying Colonus.

Let us pass to Euripides: the chorus in which he described how Apollo came to Creusa on the Acropolis, where Ion was afterwards born:

ἦλθες μοι χρυσῷ χαίταν
μαρμαίρων, εὖτ' ἐς κόλπους
κρόκεα πέταλα φάρεσιν ἔδρεπον
ἀνθίζειν χρυσανταυγή.[23]

'*Crocus chrysanthus*', proceeds Thiselton-Dyer, rather as though the choruses of Sophocles and Euripides were a Barr's bulb catalogue. The botanist here has got the better of the classic. And this is not all! '*Crocus chrysanthus*', he continues: 'a mountain species'. It is indeed. It is so 'mountain' that it does not even grow on the mountains round Athens, let alone on the Acropolis, a mere rock. It grows, in fact, only on one mountain, Parnassus.[24] I have found it under clumps of Apollo firs above Delphi, between the top of the κακὴ σκάλα and the cave of Pan. Now Delphi is the stage of Ion: was it this that misled Thiselton-Dyer? Did he forget, when he made his astonishing attribution, that Creusa's 'crocuses' grew on the Acropolis? Besides, *Crocus aureus* and *Crocus chrysanthus* are very much alike: *Crocus chrysanthus* is paler and even smaller than *Crocus aureus*, but the difference is too slight to warrant a poetical distinction; they are however alike in this, that they both grow sparsely dotted about, as units, never in masses as crocuses in an English garden, let alone a London park. This is a fatal objection, for both

19 *Anth.*, IV.1.12.

20 *O.C.*, 682 ff.

21 These two species are so similar that E. von Halácsy, *Conspectus Florae Graecae*, III (Leipzig, 1904), did not distinguish between them. I refer to both as *Crocus aureus*, the commoner species.

22 Halácsy, III, p. 195.

23 *Ion*, 887.

24 'ad nives deliquescentes regionis abietinae ... supra Livadi', Halácsy, III, p. 194.

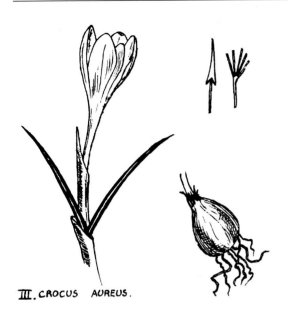

III. CROCUS AUREUS.

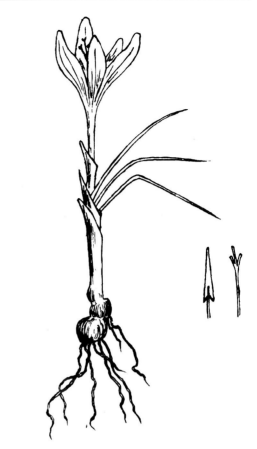

IV. CROCUS CHRYSANTHUS.

Sophocles' chorus and Euripides' chorus call up the picture of a golden sheet – of something: but of what? *Crocus gargaricus*, the only other yellow Greek crocus which 'brake like fire', would fulfil requirements admirably, but it grows only in the Troad. Leaf writes in wonder of how he saw the top of Mt Ida covered with it,[25] along with *Scilla bifolia* (ὑάκινθος) and he says that Homer must have seen it growing there, or if not Homer himself, then some predecessor who spread the tale of its glory, but that anyhow someway Homer had the summit of Ida in his mind when he wrote of the summit of Olympus:

> τοῖσι δ' ὑπὸ χθὼν δῖα φύεν νεοθηλέα ποίην,
> λωτὸν θ' ἑρσήεντα ἰδὲ κρόκον ἠδ' ὑάκινθον
> πυκνὸν καὶ μαλακόν.[26]

It is surely implicit in Leaf's rhapsody that he agrees with me that there is no likelihood that either *Crocus aureus* or *Crocus chrysanthus* inspired

Homer: it follows that he would agree that there is no likelihood that they inspired either Sophocles or Euripides. So far we are at one. But I propose to inspire Homer, and with him Sophocles and Euripides, at first hand, and without sending him to Ida.

Either Leaf, like Thiselton-Dyer, was too good a botanist to see the truth, or he never went to Greece in the autumn. For in autumn Greece produces perhaps the showiest of all its lovely shows: golden sheets of *Sternbergia sicula*, which spring up as at the wave of a magic wand after the September rains, and cover the bare foothills everywhere, in masses as big as a tennis-court.

25 W. Leaf, *Troy: a Study in Homeric Geogaphy* (London, 1912), p. 11.
26 *Il.*, XIV.347.

This *Sternbergia* is not a crocus, but a colchicum: it may be seen, a small pale ghost of its real self, in a few English gardens, but in this country it only flowers after a very hot summer. Though not a crocus, it looks like a very large, thick-petalled crocus, and I have heard it so called again and again by an unbotanical British School. It grows, says Heldreich, 'circa Athenas frequens' and he particularises Hymettus and Lycabettus and Τουρκὸ βουνὸ.[27] Now these last two are extensions of the Acropolis rock, so we are getting hot. He does not mention the Acropolis, but, in order to play the game out, I may say that I have seen *Sternbergia* there myself. Atchley showed me a patch, in October 1931, on the south side, above the theatre. So there we are, and in conclusion I would only ask any reader of this paper to remember that it was not I who in the beginning put this fairy-tale under the microscope: it was Thiselton-Dyer; and, if microscopes are applied,

then the resultant observations may just as well be accurate, specially when they are recorded in a serious compendium for the use of students.[28] And I do most seriously believe that Euripides had *Sternbergia* in his mind, and I believe Sophocles had it too, for it may well have grown upon the 'monticule' which is Colonus,[29] and I think it is Homer's crocus too, and if the κόμαι can be taken as petals (and I do not see why not, for they are sometimes leaves), then *Sternbergia* picks up my last epithet, and becomes the golden-tressed crocus of Meleager: χρυσάνθη δὲ κόμαισι κρόκον.[30] I have a slightly prosaic sorrow in the case of Sophocles, that I may have dimmed the picture: *Sternbergia* dies in December, and narcissus is not born until February; the two cannot be made to flower together; but no more could the crocus of Tennyson have flowered with amaracus and asphodel, lotus and lily. Does it really matter?

---

27 *Hodie* κρινάκι, Heldreich, Ἡ Χλωρὶς τῆς Αἰγίνης, (1898) p. 392. I regret to record that I was always told it was ζαφρονά.

28 *Ibid.*
29 *Guide Bleu*, 'Colone'.
30 *Anth.*, XII.256.7.

ALICE LINDSELL'S
BOTANICAL SKETCHBOOK

Introduced by ANTHONY BRYER

Alice Lindsell was registered as a Student of the British School at Athens for the year 1930–31, during the Directorship of Humfry Payne (1929–36). It should be explained that the 'School' is no ordinary school but an Institute of Archaeology, and that its 'Students' are no ordinary students either – for example Miss Lindsell, who in London was then Warden of Bedford College House, was almost twenty years older than her Director in Athens, who was then aged 28. But for the School and its Students, this was an exciting and exacting time, vividly described in three books by Humfry Payne's widow, Dilys Powell, *The Traveller's Journey is Done*, *The Villa Ariadne*, and *An Affair of the Heart* (many editions), and in Helen Waterhouse, *The British School at Athens. The First Hundred Years* (Thames and Hudson, 1986). Alice Lindsell's contemporaries are depicted in Rachel Hood, *Faces of Archaeology in Greece. Caricatures by Piet de Jong* (Leopard's Head Press, 1998).

Alice Lindsell's Botanical Sketchbook was found among John Raven's papers and has now been presented to Newnham College, Cambridge, where she was first registered as a student for the year 1903–4. It is a commonplace board-bound handy book, 21.5 x 14.5 cm. in size, now of 86 unnumbered folios (see pp. 23–25, 43–45 above, and p. 103 below).

Botanical sketches are in pencil and wash, evidently done on the spot, and dated from 16th October 1930 to 18th May 1931. The places named and revisited radiate from the garden of the British School at Athens itself to most classical sites then accessible, including Delos and on Crete, but omit Humfry Payne's excavation at Perachora. A favourite excursion from the B.S.A. was then by tram to the foot of Hymettos, where I take Alice Lindsell's frequent references to 'Asterie' to mean the monastery of *Asteriou* above Kaisariane. This is where in February 1675 [the Rev. Sir] George Wheler recorded no fewer than 60 "curious plants", the identification of which would have challenged John Raven, although he grew many in his gardens: (*A Journey into Greece, by George Wheler Esq; in Company of Dr Spon of Lyons* [London, 1682], pp. 413–17). But Students who used and contributed to the School's famous *Dromologue* (a running Log book of tips on how to get where and see what) were naturally more adventurous. Alice Lindsell took her paints and Sketchbook to the top of Oros in southern Aegina, then a six-hour walk and climb and still 532m. high (see p. 60).

Seven pages from Alice Lindsell's Botanical Sketchbook are in part reproduced in colour here, along with her own identifications, on the Half-title page and on pp. 59–62. The flowers at the opening of each section are also taken from Alice Lindsell's Botanical Sketchbook, but the task of identifying these plants is reserved to readers of this book.

Anthony Bryer

Clematis cirrhosa. Hymettos, 7 December 1930; f.22r

Cyclamen latifolium. British School at Athens, 22 March 1931; f.21r

Arisarum vulgare. Oros, Aegina, Zeus Panhellennion, 28 November 1930; f.18v

Mandragora autumnalis. *Eleusis, 9 November 1930; f.14r.*

Iris attica. *Mone Asteriou, Kaisariane, 7 March 1931; f.37v.*

Ornithogalum nutans. Thebes, 20 March 1931; f.48r

WAS THEOCRITUS A BOTANIST?

ALICE LINDSELL

Reprinted from *Greece and Rome*, 6, (1937), 78–93, by kind permission of
Oxford University Press

Theocritus sings of eighty-seven different trees, shrubs, flowers, grasses, and ferns. Practically all the references are in the *Pastoral Idylls*: that is to say, that in the small compass of about 1,200 lines he mentions nearly twice as many plants as Homer[1] does in the whole *Iliad* and *Odyssey*. Many of these plants are mentioned several times, and some many times, so the number is impressively great, and implies a great interest: an interest not shown by any other Greek poet. The selection, too, is unprecedented. The Comic Poets may write of things to eat (kitchen-garden produce); the Tragic and Lyric poets, of ceremonial adjuncts; garlands for gods, athletes, feasters (nursery-garden produce). Theocritus' plants are none of these: they are the plants of the mountains, foot-hills, meadows, and shores of the place in which he lived:

αἰγίπυρος καὶ κνύζα καὶ εὐώδης μελίτεια.

He writes of plants for their own sakes, and it is this that makes his attitude modern and interesting. Fourteen hundred years before him Minoan painters looked at plants with his eyes: except for them he is unique in Greek history.

'Most of the wild plants have no names, and few know about them', says Theophrastus in his Botany.[2] How, then, does Theocritus know about them? What has happened? Surely just Theophrastus himself. His dates are c. 370–285 B.C., so if Theocritus was born c. 310 B.C., that makes him 25 at the time of Theophrastus' death. So there is nothing anachronistic in attributing botanical knowledge to Theocritus. As to Theophrastus' botany, Sir William Thiselton-Dyer,[3] the late Curator of Kew, says:

Our knowledge of Greek Botany begins with Theophrastus. … He occupies a unique position in the history of science. He stands alone without successor for 2000 years. His methods were essentially. modern, and when the study of Botany was resumed in the Middle Ages, it advanced simply from the point where Theophrastus left it.

Further, the Lyceum was, under Theophrastus, enormously large and important. Diogenes says that as many as 2,000 students attended Theophrastus' lectures – lectures which were mostly botanical. And again more than this: it seems[4] likely that Theophrastus sent out some of these young men as travelling students, literally peripatetic, over Greece, and the Aegean, to collect specimens and to make observations for him. So an interest in Botany would be broadcast, and Cos, with its school of bright young poets, would no doubt be caught into the fashionable swing. Then, too, we must remember that Cos contained, besides the ephemeral poetical school of Philetas, that much more permanent institution, the medical school of Aesculapius: that at that school Erasistratus was a leading doctor; that Diogenes says that Erasistratus was a pupil of Theophrastus: lastly, that there is a tradition that Theocritus started his career in Cos by studying, not poetry under Philetas, but medicine under Erasistratus, along with his friend Nikias – Nikias, the established doctor of the *Idylls*. So the chain is complete, for the tradition is generally assumed as true, and Chomeley[5] supports it from some internal evidence in the idylls. The chain is complete, because the study of medicine in Theocritus' day would imply the study of plants first-hand. There are but few Greek plants which are not included in

---

1 This paper was written in August 1935, before the delivery of Professor Foster's paper on 'Trees and Plants in Homer'. [The footnotes were tidied up and expanded where possible in August 1999 – Eds .]

2 *Hist. Plant.* i. 14.4.

3 *Companion to Greek Studies*, Flora.

4 Sir Arthur Hort, Theophr. *Hist. Plant.*, introduction, p. xx.

5 xi. 71. See note *ad hoc.*

the Greek pharmacopoeia, and almost all our knowledge of them, apart from Theophrastus, comes from the doctors – from Hippocrates, Dioscorides, Galen, and the rest. I do not think it fanciful to go a step farther still, and to see a fundamental connexion between the School of Botany in Athens, and the School of Poetry in Cos. I think, in fact, that the pastoral form in which poetry flowered at the beginning of the third century was due to Theophrastus' influence, working out in this instance through the channels of art. For now at last the wild plants have names, and many know about them.

With the interest and with the background which I have postulated for him, Theocritus should be a field botanist, and should treat his plants with some degree of scientific accuracy. Is this the case? Directly this question is asked we are confronted with another question: 'How can we tell?' For between Theocritus and ourselves yawns the gulf of the ages. There are various possible bridges, but exigencies of space preclude me from discussing them. I can only state categorically that they are as good now as ever they are likely to be, and it merely remains for the editors and lexicons to make use of them. As regards Theocritus, Paley is before their time. Calverley, writing his lovely translations at his desk in England, makes amazing botanical blunders. Kynaston dabbles cheerfully in the subject, but as he is unaware of the existence of Theophrastus, or of any possible stage for Theocritus outside Sicily, his findings are, often, merely funny, while Chomeley, hardly interested, has at most a dozen botanical notes in his otherwise compendious edition.

However, with Theophrastus in hand, and with a careful eye to the historians and geographers, to vases and frescoes, to geology and to the flower names of modern Greece which have survived, not infrequently, their submergence under Romans, Slavs, Vlachs, Venetians, Franks, and Turks, we can still restore something of the flora of ancient Greece and of Sicily, and so of Theocritus.

That he has the careful and accurate eye of the botanist is easily proved. Firstly, he makes no

mistakes: not a single one. Virgil, who transplants some of his flora wholesale from Theocritus into Lombardy, does make mistakes, as is likely, since he is writing of plants he does not know. For instance, in the Fourth Eclogue:

non omnes arbusta iuvant, *humiles*que myricae.[6]

Now the tamarisk is never lowly: it is a big bush at the least, and often a small tree: and it does not grow in cultivated ground, as Virgil suggests, but in sand or on rocks. So Theocritus, in both his instances, plants it properly on the bluff of a hill, and makes it tall enough to give shade. τῇδε καθίξας, ὡς τὸ κάταντες τοῦτο γεώλοφον αἵ τε μυρῖκαι.[7] Secondly, Theocritus' epithets are instructive. These are not merely the conventional ones: they are often fresh and interesting. His poppy for instance, is not just ἐρυθρά red; it is ἀπαλά,[8] soft to the touch, an adjective used by Euripides of a baby's skin, which conveys vividly the silky feel of a poppy petal and shows he had handled it, perhaps as a specimen. His σέλινον[9] (wild celery, *Apium graveolens*) is not always merely χλωρόν, but once it is πολύγαμπτον, much twisted, an adjective applied elsewhere to a labyrinth, and very descriptive of the frilly leaves of the celery. It has its modern counterpart in the 'Imperial Curled Parsley' of Sutton's seed catalogue.

In the case of ἄγρωστις[10] (Dog's-tooth Grass, *Cynodon dactylon*) Theocritus uses a very botanical epithet: εἰλιτενής 'creeping in the marsh'; for if one looks up ἄγρωστις either in Theophrastus or in Halácsy one finds that a creeping root is characteristic. 'Dog's-tooth grass', says Theophrastus,[11] 'grows from the joints: for the roots are jointed, and from each joint it sends a shoot upwards and root downwards.' I call εἰλιτενής a botanical as

6 *Ecl.* iv. 2.
7 i. 13; v. 101.
8 xi. 57.
9 vii. 68.
10 xiii. 42.
11 *H.P.* iv. 10. 6.

opposed to a merely descriptive epithet, because of course the roots are not visible, so it seems likely that Theocritus handled the plant as a specimen, just as he must have handled the poppy.

In my last instance of epithets Theocritus, I think, marks a distinction between two species of plants. The name lotus is used in Greek for four distinct plants, which have, as Theophrastus himself points out, nothing in common beyond the name, though unbotanically they have this in common, that they are all eaten. Theocritus mentions two of these lotuses. One is the Nettle-tree (*Celtis australis*) which had a very good hard wood, often used for musical pipes. It was from this tree that Amphitryon's scabbard came: κολεόν, μέγα λώτινον ἔργον.[12] Theocritus' other lotus is the lotus of the *Iliad*, a clover, identified by Thistleton-Dyer with the Strawberry-leaved Clover (*Trifolium fragiferum*). This Theocritus calls χαμαὶ αὐξόμενος'.[13] Is this just a descriptive epithet? For a clover, *Trifolium fragiferum* grows high: or is there in the botanist's mind the picture of the other lotus he knows, the high tree, and is he not, in his choice of epithet, 'low-growing', marking a botanical distinction between the two?

Now let me try to establish Theocritus botanically on a more general ground – that of *locality*. No poet, I think, unless he had an entire familiarity with his plants, could have mentioned so many, so quietly, in so few lines. For here they are, the 87, multiplied in many instances by 2, and in some by as many as 7 or 8, never bursting out of their setting, but introduced with an assured hand, each as wanted, each in its right place. The poetry is so unaffected that one hardly notices how right the places are till one begins to investigate. Let us consider water-loving plants. The plane, for instance, is such. Theocritus knows this fact so well that his five plane-trees are all quite definitely placed beside rivers. In *Idyll* xxii[14] the White Poplar, λεύκη, grows beside them, and the White Poplar loves water as much as they themselves. In *Idyll* xviii,[15] moreover, the planes are growing beside the Spartan Eurotas – παρ' Εὐρώταο λοετροῖς, and this is geographically correct, for of Sparta Pausanias says that its planes were a marked feature: αἱ δὴ ὑψηλαὶ καὶ συνεχεῖς περὶ αὐτὸ αἱ πλάτανοι πεφύκασι.[16] Of flowers many similar instances might be given. I select one, the line I have already quoted:

καὶ μάν ἐς στομάλιμνον ἐλαύνεται ἔς τε τὰ Φύσκω,
καὶ ποτὶ τὸν Νήαιθον' ὅπη καλὰ πάντα φύοντι,
αἰγίπυρος καὶ κνύζα καὶ εὐώδης μελίτεια.[17]

'Στομάλιμνον', says Chomeley, 'the same marshy lake as mentioned in v. I46.' 'The marshy lake where all things grow in beauty' *because* they are by water, for rest-harrow and flea-bane cannot grow away from water, and balm needs at least a cool or shady place, and the poet-botanist has mentioned the fact in the one word 'Stomalimnos' [see p. 24 above].

Then think of levels! These, too, are botanically and unobtrusively correct. It is most obvious in the case of trees. It is, indeed, possible to make out a diagram of the levels at which trees grow in the eastern Mediterranean, and to show how convincingly, and rather touchingly, the trees of the poet correspond. Here I can only give three instances of trees, and one of a flower. Theophrastus gives a list of trees[18] which, he says, are peculiar to mountain country and do not grow in the plain. Theocritus mentions three of those on the list: φηγός (Valonia Oak), ἄρκευθος (Phoenician Cedar), and πρῖνος (Kermes Oak). You find, when you look into the Idylls that these three trees are either definitely staged upon a mountain or in mountainy surroundings. The single reference to φηγός[19] places it on Etna; ἄρκευθος is twice mentioned: once upon the Sila Mountains,[20] and

12 xxiv. 45.
13 xviii. 43.
14 Line 41.

15 Line 23.
16 Pausanias, iii. 14. 8.
17 iv. 23
18 *H.P.* iii. 3. 1.
19 ix. 20.
20 v. 97.

once juxtaposed with the narcissus,[21] which is in Greece a mountain flower: πρῖνος[22] grows alongside φηγός upon the Sila Mountains: so all is in order.

For my flower I select the ὑάκινθος: hyacinth is a convenient label for it. Theophrastus[23] says that there are two sorts of hyacinths, the wild and the cultivated (ἀγρία καὶ σπαρτή). The wild kind is almost certainly *Scilla bifolia*, and is the hyacinth of the *Iliad* and of Sappho. The cultivated kind is probably the wild larkspur (*Delphinium ajacis*), which shows the required marking AI, and so annexed the name 'hyacinth' from the cult of Hyacinthus. Theocritus knows both these hyacinths, and differentiates them clearly. *Scilla bifolia* is an exclusively mountain flower: Leaf found the top of Trojan Ida covered with it. So Theocritus the botanist, knowing the fact, gets Theocritus the poet to mention it, and add romance to his poetry in the doing:

ἠράσθην μὲν ἔγωγε τεοῦς, κόρα, ἁνίκα πρᾶτον
ἦνθες ἐμᾷ σὺν ματρὶ θέλοισ᾽ ὑακίνθινα φύλλα
ἐξ ὄρεος δρέψασθαι, ἐγὼ δ᾽ ὁν ἀγεμόνευον.[24]

Could it have been done better?

The wild larkspur, being cultivated, grows in meadows, which, in a mountainous land such as Greece, would be low-lying. This is Theocritus' γραπτὰ ὑάκινθος and it is mentioned in Idyll x[25] where the setting is cornfields and flower-borders: again unobtrusively right [see p. 27 above].

But it is neither on mountain peaks nor in lowland meadow that Theocritus is most at home. His real home is on the foot-hills, in the maquis. Maquis is the tangle of flowery, resinous, aromatic, and often spinous shrubs which covers the foot-hills of much of the Mediterranean. It is particularly characteristic of Greece: a significant point, for surely the most obvious botanical fact about the pastoral idylls is that they are staged, almost all,

in maquis. Its chief constituents, in Greece, are: Myrtle (μύρτος), Mastich (σχῖνος), Laurel (δάφνη), Christ's thorn (παλίουρος), Arbutus (κόμαρος), Wild Olive (κότινος), *Calicotome villosa* (ἀσπάλαθος), Tree-heath (ἐρείκη), Rosemary (λιβανωτίς), Jerusalem Sage (φλόμος), French Lavender (στοιχάς), with *Smilax aspera* (σμῖλαξ), trailing over them all: Smilax, so wrongly translated bryony by the editors of Euripides. Twelve plants in all, selected without any reference to Theocritus, yet all but two mentioned by Theocritus, many of them again and again. This is right, for it is on the foot-hills that his shepherds and goat-herds chiefly sing. But where are these foot-hills?

Here I come to the second section of my paper. Of what country does Theocritus write? What are his spheres? Has a study of his botany any bearing on the vexed question as to where the idylls were written, or on the still more vexed question as to where they are severally staged? I think it certainly has, and to such an extent that if the botany had been considered earlier, the question might not have been so long in debate. But it was not till the present century that a scientific[26] modern Greek Botany was published, and so established the vital and fundamental fact, till then entirely overlooked, that the flora of the eastern Mediterranean differs from that of the western, since it contains a large proportion of Asiatic plants whose western limit is Greece.

As to Theocritus' spheres, every one agrees that these are three, Sicily, Cos, Alexandria: but views as to the relative importance of the three have swung over in the period between Paley and Chomeley.

In the *Encyclopaedia Britannica* we find:

(a) Edition 9. the idylls refer to the life of shepherds and neatherds in the woods of Sicily. Theocritus lived in Syracuse, Cos, and Alexandria. (Emphasis on Sicily.)

(b) Edition 11. it is quite uncertain whether the bucolic

---

21 i. 133.
22 v. 95.
23 *H.P.* vi. 8. 2.
24 xi. 26.
25 Line 28.

26 E. von Halácsy, *Conspectus Florae Graecae*, I–II (Leipzig, 1900–1904).

poems were written in Cos, among a circle of poets and students, or in Alexandria, and intended for dwellers in streets. The usual view is, that Theocritus went first from Syracuse to Cos, and then took up his residence permanently in Egypt. (Emphasis on Alexandria.)

(c) Edition 14. Repeats 11, but continues: Willamowitz-Möllendorff, laying stress on the fact that the best MS. puts the poem to Ptolemy (I7) before that to Hiero (I8), puts the Egyptian period first, and supposes it to have been of very short duration: and then makes the poet, after an unsuccessful appeal to Hiero, retire to Cos for the rest of his life. (Emphasis on Cos.)

The latest view had received support from archaeology,[27] so let us assume for the moment that it is the correct one.

We get then, for Theocritus' life, the following scheme:

Childhood . . . . Syracuse
Student of Medicine
Student of Poetry . . . . . . Cos
Short middle periods . . . . Syracuse, Alexandria;
                                            or Alexandria, Syracuse
Later Life . . . . Cos

Emphasis on Cos indeed.

This scheme involves three well-defined botanical areas:

  1. Syracuse.
  2. Cos.
  3. Alexandria.

So now let us see if any plants can be isolated as peculiar to these several areas, and then consider the result in relation to the idylls.

We will take the areas in inverse relation to the number of plants they give, which means, be it understood, the number of plants which I have so far been able to differentiate. There are other suspects.

Alexandria comes first, and is very quickly disposed of, for there is not a single reference in any idyll to a peculiarly Egyptian plant: further, plants which might have grown in Egypt as well as elsewhere, such as the palm, are conspicuous by absence. This surely supports the view that Theocritus did not stay long in Alexandria, and that he certainly did not settle there. If he had, I cannot but think that palm, or silphium, or carob, or papyrus, or some such plant must have appeared somewhere on the stage, however much in the background.

Alexandria disposed of, we are left with Syracuse on the one hand and Cos on the other: Europe and Asia, as the Greeks themselves would say. And between Europe and Asia, as already indicated, a botanical gulf is fixed: the Asiatic character of the Greek flora. So it ought to be possible to tell, in the case of a writer who mentions as many plants as Theocritus, of which area he is writing.

Sicily comes next, and its list is easy too, for it contains but one solitary plant: the κάκτος:

ἀπολέιπῃ
ὥσπερ ὅϊς ποίμνας, ἃς τὸν πόδα κάκτος ἔτυψε.[28]

'κάκτος', says Kynaston brightly, 'is *Cactus Opuntia*, which has stalks composed of broad, flat leaves, and grows plentifully on Etna.' It does indeed, and all over Sicily. But *Cactus opuntia* is the prickly pear, a foreign import, and was introduced from Mexico by the Spaniards during their occupation of the island, subsequently to the discovery of America. It is, therefore, not Theocritus' κάκτος: it is the godchild merely of Theocritus' κάκτος, whose name Linnaeus bestowed upon *Cactus opuntia* in baptism. Theocritus' κάκτος is a very different plant. It is a thistle: Cardoon thistle: *Cynara cardunculus*. Theophrastus says of it, under the heading of spinous plants:[29] 'It is a plant quite different from any other; for it sends up straight from the root stems which creep on the ground' (well-adapted to prick the unwary foot) 'and its leaf is broad and spinous'. Theophrastus proceeds to explain that the κάκτος is first-cousin to the

27 W. R. Paton and E. L. Hicks, *The Inscriptions of Cos* (Oxford, 1891).

28 x. 4.
29 *H.P.* vi. 4. 10.

artichoke, but the crucial words are those with which he begins his description: ἡ δε κάκτος καλουμένη περὶ Σικελίαν μόνον, ἐν τῇ Ἑλλάδι δὲ οὐκ ἔστιν. That sounds simple and definite enough, but not so. There is a very odd fact about the κάκτος. It does not belong to Theocritus alone: his reference to it is an obvious imitation of his master, Philetas. Philetas' couplet is:

> Γηρύσαιτο δὲ νεβρός, ἀπὸ ψυχὴν ὀλέσασα,
> ὀξείης κάκτου τύμμα φυλαξαμένη.

Now how did Philetas know about the κάκτος if it is a purely Sicilian plant? His spheres, according to Strabo,[30] are Cos, Rhodes, and Alexandria: we know of no connexion with Sicily. Can it be that Theophrastus is nodding, and that the κάκτος grew in Cos, for it is widely distributed over Greece and the islands today. It seems impious to assume it. So κάκτος must just be left a mystery. What does emerge is the fact that if Philetas, the pure Greek, refers familiarly to the κάκτος, Theocritus too may be referring to it as a Greek, not as a Sicilian, so there is no evidence for making Idyll x Sicilian on the strength of it when the literary allusions mark it as Coan.

We are left, then, with a blank page for Alexandria, and one solitary ambiguous reference on the page for Sicily, and can proceed to isolate the purely Greek plants. Here I am on firmer ground, for I can say of my own knowledge that there is hardly an identifiable tree, shrub, or flower mentioned by Theocritus which is not still common in Greece today, and of these a certain number either have never grown in Sicily, or did not grow there in 300 B.C.

I. We will begin with the Plane again (*Platanus orientalis*: distinct from the London Plane, *Platanus occidentalis*). 'An Asiatic tree', says Thistleton-Dyer, 'reaching its western limit in Greece.' Theophrastus' evidence is again very definite:[31] 'In the Adriatic region they say the plane is not found,

and that it is rare throughout Italy:[32] yet there are many large rivers in both countries, in spite of which the localities do not seem to produce this tree.' This is as true today as it was then. The few planes I have seen growing up in the hills behind Syracuse, along a tributary of the Anapo, confirm the fact, for they were wretched undersized specimens, whereas in Greece the plane is one of the commoner deciduous trees, and grows to a great size. For Cos itself in antiquity we have the evidence of Hermesianax:[33]

> οἶσθα δὲ καὶ τὸν ἀοιδὸν ὃν Εὐρυπύλου πολιῆται
> Κῷοι χάλκειον στῆσαν ὑπὸ πλατάνῳ.

while for modern Cos, no visitor can miss the enormous, and incredibly ancient, plane which grows in the little square above the harbour. The villagers called it the Plane of Hippocrates, and claimed that it was as old as Hippocrates. I am told by a botanist, who has kindly investigated the point for me, that the claim is conceivably true. The trunk, however, to be the required age, should measure at least 25 feet in diameter. I shall be extremely grateful if any one who chances to read this paper, and subsequently to go to Cos, will measure the trunk. [It was 46 feet in 1997 – Eds.] The tree has this interest, that if it is really the Plane of Hippocrates, who was Theocritus' predecessor by 150 years, it is also one of the actual planes of which Theocritus writes, and he must have seen it, and sat under it a thousand times.

II. The Cypress (*Cupressus sempervirens*) is another tree unlikely to have grown in Sicily in Theocritus' day. It too is an Asiatic tree, early introduced into Greece, and there very common and beautiful. It is rare in Sicily, though in N. Italy it seems to have established itself before Virgil's time. Theophrastus[34] says that it was not generally distributed, and mentions Crete, Lydia, and

30 xiv. 2. 19.
31 *H.P.* iv. 5, 6.

32 'Italy' means S. Italy – as elsewhere in Theophrastus.
33 Athenaeus, *Deipnosophistae*, 598.
34 *H.P.* iv. 5. 2; cp. Strabo, x. 4. 4.

Rhodes as its bases: Rhodes, the island next to Cos, and Lydia and Crete both near by. The geology of Rhodes is so similar to that of Cos, that if the cypress is vouched for in the one island, it is certain to have grown also in the other. Theocritus mentions cypress no less than seven times, so he obviously lived in a land of them.

III. ἐρείκη (*Erica arborea*, Tree-heath, a maquis plant). This is an immense shrub, growing as I know it to 12 feet or more, and sometimes, according to the *Encyclopaedia Britannica*, reaching the height and aspect of a tree.[35] Only two of the poets mention Erica: Aeschylus once, in the Agamemnon,[36] where the φύλαξ of Mycenae says that the bonfires which announced the fall of Troy were made of it:

οἱ δ᾽ ἀντέλαμψαν καὶ παρήγγειλαν πρόσω
γραίας ἐρείκης θωμὸν ἄψαντες πυρί.

This is interesting because, on the mountains about Mycenae, *Erica arborea* still grows magnificently, and it is still the common or only fuel of the Argolid, and it is still called ρείκι. The other poet is, of course, Theocritus himself:

ἀλλὰ τὸν ἄνδρα
εἰ λῇς, τὸν δρυτόμον βωστρήσομες, ὃς τὰς ἐρείκας
τήνας τὰς παρὰ τὶν ξυλοχίζεται[37]

That this ἐρείκη is tree-heath, and not one of the small Sicilian heaths, is proved by the fact that it is being dealt with by a wood-cutter: though Calverley, if you please, translates 'bracken'. Now tree-heath is not a Syracusan plant: it does not like a limey soil, but flourishes rather on gneiss or schist. There is one such area near Messina, and there alone in all Sicily does *Erica arborea* grow. Messina is out of Theocritus' range, of course, but in any case it is in Idyll v that the ἐρείκη grows, and Idylls iv and v are both staged on the Sila Mountains of S. Italy, which are not lime-

stone like Syracuse, but gneiss like the parts about Messina and much of Greece, so it is correctly placed.

IV. From the wild maquis we turn to cultivated food plants, and first to the most important of them: πυρός, wheat. Theocritus has little to say about it. He mentions the πυροφόροι γύαι,[38] the legendary acres of Augeas, and he has one non-commital reference to ἄλευρον,[39] wheatflour. But it is barley in its various forms: κρῖθι, ἄλφιτα, μᾶζα – which is his known food, and it is for barley that thanks are offered at his harvest-home:

μάλα γάρ σφιζι πίονι μέτρῳ
ἀ δαίμων εὔκριθον ἀνεπλήρωσεν ἀλωάν.[40]

since with no grudging hand
Hath the boon goddess filled the *wheaten* floor.

says Calverley: a significant mistranslation, for it shows that he, a daily eater of white bread, thinks that at this festival too much emphasis is placed on mere barley. Certainly any Syracusan would have agreed with Calverley. Barley grew in Sicily, of course:[41] it appears to have grown in all Mediterranean countries from the earliest times: but the wheat of Sicily was famous. And of all Sicily the plain which lies around Syracuse was the most productive. Freeman[42] says in his day the good wheat of Syracuse was sold in Naples, and the bad wheat of Italy brought back in exchange. 'The Sicilian wheat', says Theophrastus,[43] 'is heavier than most of that imported into Hellas.' It was surpassed only by the wheat of Boeotia, which was so good that athletes there could only absorb three pints of it a day, whereas, when they came to Athens, they could easily consume five. There is, however no evidence that Boeotian wheat was

35 Cp. Plutarch, *de Iside*, 357 A.
36 Aeschylus, *Agamemnon*, 295.
37 v. 64.

38 xxv. 30.
39 xiv. 7.
40 vii. 34.
41 Pliny, *N. H.*, xviii. 84.
42 E. A. Freeman, *History of Sicily*, I (London, 1891), p. 92.
43 *H.P.* viii. 4. 5.

exported, even over the border into Attica.[44] Elsewhere in Greece, with the exception of the Plain of Thessaly, there was little wheat, and that very poor, so barley, which yielded a fair return on any soil, was everywhere cultivated, and formed the staple food of the people. Pliny,[45] as Thiselton-Dyer points out, notes the difference between Greece and Italy in this respect: 'Videtur tam puls ignota Graeciae fuisse quam Italiae polenta.' *Polenta* of course = ἄλφιτα = barley-groats. So Theocritus' barley festival is as natural and right for Greece as it would be wrong for Italy in general, and for Sicily in particular, and botany fixes Idyll vii as Greek just as certainly as archaeology.

V. Still in the food category comes that interesting little plant, cummin (*Cuminum cyminum*), from W. Asia. Theophrastus[46] says that its seeds were very small and very numerous: they were also very cheap, which explains why Aristophanes calls one miser κυμινοπρίστης, and why Theocritus[47] sarcastically warns another miser: μήτι τάμῃς τὰν χεῖρα καταπρίων τὸ κύμινον. Cummin was a favourite seasoning in Greece, and was considered particularly tasty with fish. The Comic Poets are full of jokes about it. But if we accept the argumentum ab silentio, it did not reach Italy till some time after Theocritus, and was probably not introduced there till after the Roman occupation of Greece, which began in 146 B.C. The first mention of it in Roman literature is in Horace:[48] 'biberent exsangue cuminum', and in Italy it seems to have been used exclusively as a drug: not as a condiment.

VI. From food for man we turn to food for beast: κύτισος (*Medicago arborea*, Tree-medic) a plant allied to Aristophanes' μηδική or πόα μηδική, our lucerne. It is a tallish shrub with yellow flowers. 'It riseth up to the height of a man at most', Parkinson says, and today Greek monks make their rosary beads from its stem. It is native to Greece. It was first cultivated on the islands, and later all over the mainland, and no wonder, for it grew easily on any soil, and provided excellent fodder for sheep, goats, oxen, horses, swine, fowls, and bees: so it merits Pliny's tribute: 'Miris laudibus praedicatus pabulo omnium.'[49] Pliny further says 'since it has been transplanted to the cities of Greece, it has greatly increased the supply of cheese: considering this, I am surprised that it is so rarely used in Italy.'[50]

Theocritus mentions cytisus twice: both times as a goat food, and both times as a well-known food. In Idyll v:[51]

ταὶ μὲν ἐμαὶ κύτισόν τε καὶ αἴγιλον αἶγες ἔδοντι

and again in Idyll x [52]

ἁ αἲξ τὸν κύτισον ὁ λύκος τὰν αἶγα διώκει.

'Theocritus,' says Sergeaunt, 'here writes as an eye-witness'; he has seen the unwary goat cropping the cytisus and the wolf stealing down the mountain-side upon it. Virgil[53] has not seen this sight, though he writes as if he had, in his rather clumsy imitation:

Torva leaena lupum sequitur, lupus ipse capellam,
Florentem cytisum sequitur lasciva capella.

but here again, as with tamarisk, Virgil is borrowing the unknown from Theocritus, for cytisus, though now fairly common in Sicily, was not introduced till long after Theocritus' day, and it has never grown in the Cisalpine province.

I end my list with two coronary flowers.

44 E. C. Sempel, *The Geography of the Mediterranean Region* (New York, 1931), p. 353.
45 *N.H.* xviii. 19.
46 *H.P.* vii. 3. 3.
47 x. 55.
48 *Epist.* i. 19. 18.

49 *N.H.* xiii. 47. 130.
50 *N.H.* xiii. 47. 134.
51 v. 128
52 x. 30.
53 *Ecl.* iii. 63.

VII. ἄνηθον. 'This', says Kynaston, 'is not *Anethum graveolens*, Dill, which is unknown in Sicily, but probably *Anethum foeniculum*, Fennel.' But why? Fennel is as common in Greece as it is in Sicily:[54] the Plain of Marathon was so called from the sheets of fennel (μάραθον) which grew in it. Theophrastus mentions dill and fennel side by side: τοῦ σελίνου ἀνήθου, μαράθου,[55] and as he knew both plants, of course Theocritus knew them too, and when he says dill, he means dill, and not another plant. Dill was, in fact, not only known, but well known, and was in demand for garlands on account of its sweet smell: a garland of fennel is not an attractive thought. Sappho and Alcaeus both make wreaths of dill, as does Theocritus.[56] It provides yet another instance in which Virgil borrows from Theocritus a flower to him unknown:

> florem jungit bene olentis anethi.[57]

VIII. Ἴον, the purple violet (*Viola odorata*), is my second flower. 'Generally rendered violet', proceeds Kynaston, 'but it is doubtful whether it should not rather be rendered iris, because the *violet is exceedingly rare in Sicily, and of late introduction*, whereas the iris is very common, growing wild in great profusion.' I, of course, say: 'Let us continue to render ἴον violet, since in Greece it grew and grows wild in great profusion, and, once Theocritus is shifted to Greece, presents no difficulty.' For the plant which Theophrastus describes as ἴον is the purple violet, beyond doubt. Greece today is a land of violets. Even in the scorched Attic plain they are to be picked in handfuls, under their strange Turkish name μινεξέδες [*menekşe*, Farsi *benefshe*], while in Arcadia, where they are still firmly called ἴα, they grow in unforgettable sheets, at a time when, between Syracuse and Etna, not a trace of them is visible outside gardens. So

here is a fundamental and permanent contrast between the two countries. Theocritus mentions the ἴον three times, and obviously knows it well, as in

> καὶ τὸ ἴον καλόν ἐστιν ἐν εἴαρι, καὶ ταχὺ γηρᾷ:

a lovely line, which is surely his, however spurious most of Idyll xiii.

We have, then, eight plants which are Greek, and which are not Sicilian: Plane, Cypress, Tree-heath, Barley, Cummin, Tree-medic, Dill, Violet. These eight are mentioned in all twenty-five times, so it is a fair number with which to generalize. Of these twenty-five mentions, three alone occur in Sicilian surroundings. Cypresses grow on Etna in Idyll ii: goats crop the tree-medic of Croton in Idyll v: a violet is mentioned in the dirge for Sicilian Daphnis in Idyll i. The twenty-two other plants all grow either on soil certified Greek or Asiatic, or on unnamed soil, where they should, if I am right, be useful as fixing their respective idylls as Greek-staged. As for the three misplacements, tree-heath is a definite blunder. I do not feel so sure about the cypress; it may have grown sparingly in Sicily, then as now; my point about the cypress was that, as Theocritus mentions it so often, he must have lived in a land of them, which Greece was, and which Sicily was not. As for the violet, νῦν δ' ἴα μὲν φορέοιτε βάτοι: that really is a non-committal reference: a different thing from saying: νῦν δ' ἴα μὲν φορέουσι βάτοι. It might, indeed, be argued that the general upset in Nature caused by Daphnis' death would be increased if brambles burst, not only into flower, but into an alien flower; but this, perhaps, is going a little far! In any case, the setting of Idyll i is admittedly Greek: it is the dirge only which is Sicilian, and this makes the trespass of a Greek flower natural and pardonable. So I suggest we let off Theocritus with $1^1/_2$ bad marks (a low percentage out of a possible 25); 1 for tree-heath, $^1/_2$ for violet: and many congratulations for coming so well through the test.

From another point of view he comes through even better. I was very much impressed, when in the parts around Syracuse, on seeing how different

54 Strabo, iii. 4. 9.
55 *H.P.* i. 2. 2.
56 vii. 63. 2
57 *Ecl.* ii. 48.

the flora looked from that of Greece, though on paper the two countries share so much. For one thing there is no maquis, and can never have been much: for another, the proportion varies enormously: many plants common in Greece are uncommon, even though they may exist, in Sicily, and vice versa: so that, even without my eight peculiar plants as a check, I should personally be sure that the background of all pastoral idylls was Greece, however much, in four of them, Sicilian shepherds and shepherdesses masquerade upon it, since the background in all of them is (a) the same; (b) painted quite invariably with the most common and characteristic plants of Greece. If Theocritus' flora is typically Greek it cannot also be Sicilian, given this difference in proportion, and given the large Asiatic element in the Greek flora.

I should not, in fact, have been disconcerted to find more Greek plants growing in Sicilian soil than those which do so grow, for the following reason:

There appear to be three grades in the pastoral idylls:

A. The so-called 'bucolic masquerade': Theocritus and his friends featuring as peasants.
   Background: definitely Cos. Content: Idyll vii.
B. The genuine pastoral; local unidealized peasants.
   Background: definitely S. Italy. Content: Idylls iv, v.
C. A class between A and B. Pseudo-peasants, inclining sometimes to A, as in Idyll i: sometimes to B, as in Idyll x: i.e. less or more realistic, but with little fundamental difference in treatment.
   Background: Sicily. Content : Idylls i, viii, ix, xi.
   – Background: unspecified, but with literary allusions which point to Cos. Content: Idylls iii, vi, x.

Yet Class C, by the consensus of modern scholarship, English and German, reinforced by archaeology, were all written in Cos, more or less at one time, and that time the same as Class A, Idyll vii,

whose background is indubitably Cos. We have, therefore, in Classes A and C a group of poems, all written in Cos, written about the same sort of people, staged on a background which is always the same, which is four times called Sicily, once Cos, and otherwise not definitely indicated, and this background, whether called Sicily, Cos, or nothing, adorned invariably with a flora which is obviously Greek. Surely in every case Theocritus is writing in Greece, of Greeks who live in Greece, though in four cases Sicilian names are given to features in the background. If so, it is as a geographer, rather than a botanist, that Theocritus fails in scientific accuracy. But is it not all perfectly natural? He left Sicily an untrained boy. His training, medical, botanical, poetical, was Greek. His surroundings, when he came to write, were Greek, and would naturally become the background of his writings. But though Greece had his eyes, his ears, his mind, his tongue, I think that Sicily, and Etna which dominates his Sicily, retained his heart. He writes of Sicily with enthusiasm often: a thing he never does of Greece. He writes of it on an almost homesick note sometimes:

ἀλλ᾽ ὑπὸ τᾷ πέτρᾳ τᾷδ᾽ ἄσομαι, ἀγκὰς ἔχων τυ,
οὐννομα μῆλ᾽ ἐσορῶν, τὰν Σικελὰν ἐς ἅλα.[58]

and may not the passion in his appeal to Hiero for employment be in part the cry of the exile for his home? Then let his Sicilian staging be the outcome of this feeling: a tribute to the country of his birth. For love of it, let us say, he gives Sicilian names to Greek landscapes: he does not deck Sicilian landscapes with Greek flowers. His cypresses are not misplaced: they are indeed growing round him, for the mountain behind them is Greek; it is the Prion of Cos: its name only is Sicilian, Etna: and so with the other Sicilian place-names. Apart from the actual pastorals, the idylls are all staged either in Greece or Asia Minor, so there is no further possibility of botanical error.

I hope it may be thought that a claim has been

58 viii. 56.

established for a measure of botanical knowledge on the part of Theocritus, given his early date, and in comparison with Virgil, who, two and a half centuries later, handles somewhat unconvincingly an alien flora. I hope, too, it may be thought that an inquiry into the plants of Theocritus has this value, that it does support absolutely the modern metamorphosis of him from a Sicilian writing in Sicily, of Sicily, for Sicilians or Alexandrians, into a Sicilian writing in Greece, of Greeks, for Greeks. The old view was held unquestioningly through the centuries: it was stated as lately as 1897 by Professor Gilbert Murray in his *Greek Literature*: it was assumed even by Sergeaunt in 1920; but the plants of Theocritus alone disprove it, since they contain species which a poet whose range was bounded by Sicily could never have known: a poet, that is, who, unlike Virgil, has no predecessor from whom to borrow, since he is himself the first of the pastoral poets, and the source of the pastoral poetry of the world.

LECTURE TO THE ALPINE GARDEN SOCIETY OF OXFORD

(Wednesday, 10th February, 1971)

JOHN RAVEN with photographs by FAITH RAVEN

Here I am on completely false pretences: not a botanist at all, but a full-time lecturer in classics at Cambridge with a mild taste for plant-hunting, especially in the hills, and for gardening. It so happens that this term and next I have been granted leave of absence for the purpose of writing a book, long needed by students both of classics and of science, on the history of botany in ancient Greece, the identity of the eight hundred-odd plants mentioned in extant Greek literature, and the veracity or otherwise of statements made about those plants in ancient books. Unfortunately the task of identification is proving much more difficult than I had anticipated; not only are the descriptions of a plant often hard to reconcile one with another, but also I am becoming increasingly convinced that in many cases the same Greek name covers a number of distinct plants. Our own familiar bluebell, which means one thing to the English and quite another to the Scots, is bad enough in that respect; but it is nothing to the ancient hyacinth, the colour of which is described by various authors as anything from white or blue, through purple and rust-coloured, to black, and which has accordingly been identified in modern times with almost any plant you can think of, ranging from larkspur to gladiolus. But despite the difficulties, I am plodding hopefully on – I have, for instance, satisfied myself that the ancient hyacinth was actually some species of terrestrial orchid, possibly the very variable *Orchis quadripunctata*, which is widespread in Greece – and I find the subject so intriguing that I propose, with no conscience whatever, to pin my talk this evening, albeit very lightly, on to its fringe.

At first hearing it is perhaps a surprising fact that of all the sciences practiced in antiquity botany is the one whose history can be most continuously reconstructed. But the reason for that is not far to seek. From time immemorial right down to the present day, when it is represented by Culpeper

House, the fraternity of herbalists has been assiduously gathering and drying its medicaments and purveying them to a credulous public. Indeed Theophrastus, the so-called father of botany, of whom more very soon, tells us in the ninth and last book of his *History of Plants* something of the time-honoured practices of this venerable profession. Here are some extracts from his statements and comments, translated by Sir Arthur Hort, about the ancient brotherhood of ῥιζοτόμοι or root-cutters and φαρμακοπώλαι or druggists:

Further we may add statements made by druggists and herb-diggers, which in some cases may be to the point, but in others contain exaggeration. Thus they enjoin that in cutting some roots one should stand to the windward, – for instance, in cutting *thapsia* among others, and that one should first anoint oneself with oil, for that one's body will swell up if one stands the other way. Also that the fruit of the wild rose must be gathered standing to windward, since otherwise there is danger to the eyes … they say that the peony, which some call *glykyside*, should be dug up at night, for, if a man does it in the day-time and is observed by a woodpecker while he is gathering the fruit, he risks the loss of his eyesight; and, if he is cutting the root at the time, he gets *prolapsus ani* … One should also, it is said, draw a circle round the black hellebore and cut it standing towards the east and saying prayers, and one should look out for an eagle both on the right and on the left; for that there is danger to those that cut, if your eagle should come near, that they may die within the year. (*H.P.* ix, pp. 257–61)

Terrible indeed the hazards to which the band of professional root-cutters gallantly exposed themselves, foolhardy the amateur who tried to cash in on the proceeds of their courage. And what manifold benefits they bestowed upon mankind. Listen for example to the string of ailments, in man and beast alike, that are cured by the single drug appropriately called πάνακες or all-heal:

Various parts of all-heal are also useful, and not all for the same purposes; the fruit is used in cases of miscarriage and for disorders of the bladder, while the juice, which is also called *khalbane*, is used in cases of miscarriage and also for sprains and such-like troubles; also for the ears, and to strengthen the voice. The root is used in childbirth, for diseases of women, and for flatulence in beasts of burden. (*H.P.* ix, pp. 261–3)

Not even the manufacturers of Aspirin can compete with that by way of advertisement.

And yet, in the midst of all this mumbo-jumbo, there were evidently some of the fraternity who indulged in experiment and empiricism. Theophrastus again, in a later chapter of the same book, has preserved for us the following fascinating information:

For it seems that some poisons become poisonous because they are unfamiliar, or perhaps it is a more accurate way of putting it to say that familiarity makes poisons non-poisonous; for, when the constitution has accepted them and prevails over them, they cease to be poisons, as Thrasyas also remarked; for he said that the same thing was a poison to one and not to another; thus he distinguished between different constitutions, as he thought was right; and he was clever at observing the differences. Also, besides the constitution, it is plain that use has something to do with it. At least Eudemus, the vendor of drugs, who had a high reputation in his business, after making a wager that he would experience no effect before sunset, drank a quite moderate dose, and it proved too strong for his power of resistance: while the Chian Eudemus took a draught of hellebore and was not purged. And on one occasion he said that in a single day he took two and twenty draughts in the market-place as he sat at his stall, and did not leave the place till it was evening, and then he went home and had a bath and dined, and was not sick. However this man was able to hold out because he had provided himself with an antidote; for he said that after the seventh dose he took a draught of tart vinegar with pumice-stone dust in it, and later on took a draught of the same in wine in like manner; and that the virtue of the pumice-stone dust is so great that, if one puts it into a boiling pot of wine, it causes it to cease to boil, not merely for the moment, but altogether, clearly because it has a drying effect and it catches the vapour and passes it off. It was then by this antidote that Eudemus was able to contain himself in spite of the large quantity of hellebore which he took. (*H.P.* ix, 17, pp. 305–7)

It is a pity that the experimental curiosity of these men did not find expression on a somewhat higher plane.

Now, what was this potent drug ἐλλέβορος? Seeing that in the first passage I read it is explicitly called black hellebore, it is tempting to jump to the conclusion that it is obviously the plant which Linnaeus called by the same name, *Helleborus niger* or the Christmas rose. But that obvious solution founders on the simple snag that the Christmas rose is unknown in Greece. Our own photograph of it, which I include only because they show how, when the flowers are over, the sepals of the wild plant turn an attractive shade of terra-cotta, was taken a fortnight after last Easter, slightly to the South of its centre of distribution, in the hills of northern Italy. On the whole the strongest candidate for the title of black hellebore would appear to be *Helleborus cyclophyllus*, which extends its range from Turkey across northern Greece (our photographs of it were actually taken in the deciduous woods of Macedonia) and at the westernmost limit of its distribution, in north-eastern Italy, assumes such a different appearance that it has been raised to specific rank under the name of *Helleborus odorus*. And included in the ancient black hellebore was probably also *Helleborus orientalis*, the parent of many splendid garden hybrids, which also just extends from Turkey to Greece and which we found to our surprise, thereby greatly extending its known range to the South-East, in a shady hollow in the middle of the isle of Corfu. Incidentally, the four roots of it we brought back with us are invariably in full flower by the middle of November and it is thus appreciably the earliest of all the many hellebores we grow.

So much for the black hellebore; but what of the white? The situation is complicated rather than eased by a last passage from the ninth book of Theophrastus which runs as follows:

The white and the black hellebore appear to have nothing in common except the name. But accounts differ as to the appearance of the plants; some say that the two are alike and differ only in colour; some however say

Helleborus niger

that the leaf of the 'black' is like that of bay, that of the 'white' like that of the leek, but that the roots are alike except for their respective colour. Now those who say that the two plants are alike describe the appearance as follows: the stem is like that of asphodel and very short; the leaf has broad divisions, and is extremely like that of ferula, but is long; it is clearly attached to the root and creeps on the ground; the plant has numerous roots, to wit, the slender roots which are serviceable. (*H.P.* ix, 10, pp. 265–7)

The imagination boggles at the description given by those who conflate the two kinds of hellebore into a single plant: what plant can ever have existed with tightly curved leaves like the giant fennel and a stem like that of asphodel? It seems safer to follow those who say that 'the leaf of the white hellebore is like that of the leek', and that 'it

is at its prime in autumn and past its prime when spring comes'. With those two clues available, I am at a loss to understand how the latest authority on ancient Greek plant names, Sir William Thiselton-Dyer, came to identify the white hellebore with *Veratrum album*. As our photograph of the *Veratrum album* in the Val d'Isère may suffice to show, its leaves bear only the remotest resemblance (if indeed that) to those of a leek, while the same photograph, which was taken at a high altitude at the very beginning of July, shows the plant past full flower at least three months earlier than Theophrastus tells us it should be. My own guess, for what it is worth, is that the white hellebore of the ancients is *Urginea maritima*. A photograph of it shows that its leaves, which only appear, like those of *Colchicum*, after the flowering season, do

81

Helleborus cyclophyllus

indeed bear a tolerable likeness to those of the leek.

I have dallied too affectionately with these ancient root-cutters; I must not only move on to Theophrastus himself, I must try and see to it that he does not detain us too long. Born in 370 B.C. in the island of Mitylene, alias Lesbos, he was sent by his ambitious parents, while still a boy, to study philosophy under Plato in the Academy (with a capital A of course, meaning the precinct of the hero Academicus in which the school was built, and the prototype of all subsequent academies). There he met Aristotle, the dominant influence throughout his whole long life, who, though his senior by fifteen years, was still at this stage his fellow pupil under Plato. When, however, Plato died and Aristotle, passed over for the headship of the Academy for family and political reasons, left the school to found one of his own called the Lyceum, Theophrastus went with him and under his guidance embarked on a programme of collaborative research without precedent in the history of European thought. Among his multifarious activities, which stamp him as possibly the greatest if not the most congenial philosopher of all times, Aristotle himself, incredibly, found time to put on papyrus the stupendous treatises, the *History of Animals,* the *Generation of Animals,* and the *Movement of Animals,* which represent not only the birth of the science of zoology, but its instantaneous advance to something very like maturity. But even for Aristotle there was a limit to the number of detailed studies that he could undertake at the same time, and the plant kingdom was the one that he chose to delegate. Theophrastus, the favourite pupil to whom he eventually handed on the headship of the Lyceum, was evidently charged to do for plants much what Aristotle

Veratrum album in the Val d'Isère

Urginea maritima

himself had already done for animals, for birds, for fishes and for insects.

It is no slight on Theophrastus to say that he lacked the unprecedented biological insight of his master. Enthusiasm and industry he had in abundance, and he was blessed with a long enough life to indulge them to the full; according to a passage in his best known work, that study of the diversity of human nature entitled the *Characters,* he was still lecturing and scribbling away, poor soul, at the age of ninety-nine. But we may still fairly doubt whether, but for the overpowering influence of Aristotle, he would even have had the initiative or the inclination to embark on his two monumental treatises, the *History of Plants* and the *Causes of Plants,* fifteen whole books between them, on the diversity of vegetable nature. At all events, in the outcome he is debarred from successfully emulating Aristotle by two particular failures. In the first place, it seems never to have entered his head that sex plays as important a part in the reproduction of plants as in that of animals; though he not infrequently speaks of plants as male and female, the most cursory reading of the passages in question reveals that the female is of a different species, if not indeed of a different genus or even family, from the male. Admittedly, before the days of the microscope or lens, and even since those days, the sex organs of a flower by no means obviously betray their vital function. However, in one who got so far as to list, in the very first sentence of Book II of the *History of Plants,* 'the ways in which trees and plants in general originate' as 'spontaneous growth, growth from seed, from a root, from a cutting' and so on, and immediately goes on to say that 'growth from seed would seem most natural', it is provoking to find no glimmering of the notion that the seed might be, as it is in the animal kingdom that Aristotle had so thoroughly explored and expounded, produced through the omnipresent agency of sex.

But Theophrastus' second main shortcoming is both more damaging and more relevant: never, despite incessant efforts, does he light upon at all an adequate natural system of classification.

Though at various times he plays with the common popular distinction between flowering and flowerless, fruiting and non-fruiting, or terrestrial, marsh-loving, aquatic and marine, the two bases for classification that he seems to have found most alluring are the divisions, first, into trees, shrubs, sub-shrubs and herbs, and second, horror of horrors, into cultivated and wild. This last seems almost incredible in one who not only built up the prototype of all botanical gardens in Europe, but who evidently loved it so much that in his will, among other careful provisions for its maintenance and profitable use, he wrote as follows: 'I desire to be buried in any part of the garden that they (that is, seven named colleagues and friends) shall think most suitable, charging them not to be at any superfluous expense upon either my funeral or my tomb'. And I need hardly add, to such an audience at least, that this last distinction between cultivated and wild, though more obviously preposterous than the others entertained as possible bases for classification, is actually no wider the mark than any of the rest.

And yet, once again, there are grounds for irritation that Theophrastus, with the facilities that he had laid on for himself in his garden, did not come nearer to an explicit formulation of the scientific method of botanical classification. The point is that time and again there are implicit suggestions that he is about to enunciate a fundamental truth, but time and again he lacks the courage of his convictions and shies away from the truly scientific distinctions which he seems about to draw in favour of an unscientific or artificial one. So, for instance, having in one brief section grouped together and succinctly and accurately distinguished between the Yellow Horned Poppy of the sea shore and the Red Poppy of the barley fields which he actually calls ῥοιάς, he is most intelligently and promisingly led by the similarity of the shape and structure of their respective capsules to talk in the very next section of, first, the yellow water lily, νυμφαία, and then of birthwort, ἀριστολόχια. And so again he occasionally coins, and thereafter uses frequently, an adjective which, though he perversely refrains from employing it in that way, could have perfectly well served as the name of a true botanical family. One such adjective is καλαμώδης, reed-like, the Greek equivalent of *Arundinaceae*; another is ἀκανθώδης, thistle-like; and a third, which for your sake rather than my own I propose to make the occasion for a blatant diversion, is ναρθηκώδης, like νάρθηξ or *Ferula communis*, which, from his very usage of the word, is unmistakably Theophrastus' anticipation of the Linnaean *Umbelliferae*.

Here, then, is a photograph, taken in early April on top of Mount Filerimo in Rhodes, of the magnificent νάρθηξ or *Ferula communis*. No wonder Theophrastus took it as his yardstick of what an umbelliferous plant should be or that Prometheus chose its hollow great trunk of a stem as the vehicle in which to convey stolen fire from heaven to earth. In a curious gardening book that I wrote for the good of my health last winter I bewailed the fact that no British nurseryman had the initiative to introduce this noble plant into commerce; whereupon my old friend Tom Tutin, who kindly read the page-proofs, wrote and said that as it was perfectly hardy in Leicester he would be sending me seed of it in time for spring sowing. And now that I have begun to digress, here is another and more familiar giant umbellifer in *Heracleum mantegazzianum*, a plant which, despite its recent notoriety, has never done any of my family, all of whom handle it very freely, the slightest harm. And here there is another exquisite member of Theophrastus' ναρθηκώδαι, the Himalayan *Selinum tenuifolium*, the very existence of which, until I rubbed his nose in this very plant of it last summer, was hotly denied by no less an authority than the said Tom Tutin. And coming nearer to home, here is a native of our British coasts, the familiar sea-holly, *Eryngium maritimum*, an inhabitant of sandy beaches in the South. Incidentally Theophrastus may be forgiven for placing Eryngium, on the only occasion he mentions it, cheek by jowl with a couple of thistles. The plant he had in mind was doubtless the very rare British native *Eryngium campestre*, which is

abundant around the Mediterranean and was actually introduced into our garden, where it does almost too well, from Provence. But, as the next slide shows, any eryngium bears a much stronger superficial resemblance to a thistle than to an average umbellifer. Here is that superb biennial from the Caucasus, *Eryngium giganteum*, better known as Miss Wilmott's Ghost, which sows itself so profusely in our light dry chalky soil, and especially in gravel paths, that we have had to have recourse to weedkiller in our efforts to restrain it. Next, just to show the versatility of the *Umbelliferae*, here [on p. 92] is a photograph of the familiar *Astrantia major*, another plant that sows itself all over the place with us.

And that is enough of Theophrastus and of the irrelevances he suggests to me; it is high time we turned on to the only other major botanical writer of ancient Greece whose works have come down to us, the herbalist Dioscorides. Dioscorides was a physician attached, in the ancient equivalent of the Royal Army Medical Corps, to the armies of the notorious Roman emperor Nero, and, as such, he perforce travelled at least as far as India. On his travels he evidently collected plants for medicinal purposes and tried them out on his unfortunate patients, while in his hours of leisure he must have composed his herbal. This curious work happens, by the purest accident, to be the earliest European publication of its kind to have survived; but it undoubtedly owes a large debt to several earlier Greek herbals, notably one by Cratevas, which have all alike perished. Although until very lately it was the medical bible of, for instance, the monks of Mount Athos, it is for the most part a nauseating mixture of obscenity and superstition. But despite the welter of magical mumbo-jumbo, it has two great compensating merits. In the first place it gives us a number of tolerably vivid thumb-nail sketches both of plants, of which Dioscorides mentions well over five hundred, and of their habitats; of these more anon. And in the second place there is an occasional paragraph which points unmistakably to a modicum of empirical observation. Thus, to give the obvious

Ferula communis on Mount Filerimo, Rhodes

Heracleum mantegazzianum

Selinum tenuifolium

Eryngium maritinum

Eryngium campestre

Eryngium giganteum

illustration, he described in some detail the extraction and decoction from either *Mandragora officinarum* or *Mandragora autumnalis* or both, alias mandrake (a Greek species of the same family as contains the true deadly nightshade, the potato and the tobacco plant), of a drug which, in an early translation of his own words, 'should be given to such as shall be cut or cauterised. For they do not apprehend the pain, because they are overborn with dead sleep … A man sleeps in ye same fashion as when he ate it, sensible of nothing for 3 or 4 hours from ye time that it is brought to him'. So, almost exactly nineteen hundred years before the elaborate celebration of the first centenary of the discovery of anaesthetics, Dioscorides anticipated the modern use of the extract from another plant of the same family, the preliminary anaesthetic popularly known as Twilight Sleep.

The paragraphs which, after a good deal of thought, I have chosen to illustrate Dioscorides' method and style are those comprising Chapter 165 of Book IV and dealing with the various species of what he follows Theophrastus in calling τιθύμαλλος, and what we call *Euphorbia* or spurge. As a matter of fact Dioscorides does use the word εὐφόρβιον too and applies it to one of the tree spurges of North Africa; and what is more, he vividly and accurately describes the blistering effects of its potent juice, or, as he puts it, its 'very sharp liquor'. But not unnaturally he failed to realise that the tree spurges were congeneric with the herbaceous, which he therefore continued to call τιθύμαλλος and divided into seven species. This is how his chapter on the subject begins, again in the translation of John Goodyer which dates from 1655:

91

Astrantia major

Mandragora officinarum

Of Tithymal there are 7 kinds: of which ye male is called Characias …, ye other, female, Myrtites … or Myrsinites, ye 3rd Paralius, ye 4 Helioscopius, ye 5 Cyparissias, ye 6 Dendroides, ye 7 Platyphyllos.

From as early a date as about 50 A.D. you could hardly ask for a more modern-sounding list than that; and to judge from the individual descriptions that follow, Linnaeus in this case at least correctly identified most of the seven and rightly perpetuated their ancient names. Here is a photograph of the first of them, *Euphorbia characias,* taken at Mistra near Sparta, and this is what Dioscorides says about the plant:

of that which is called Characias, ye stalks are above a cubit, red, full of sharp & white juice. But ye leaves about ye rods, like ye Olive but longer & narrower, ye root gross and woody. But on ye top of ye stalks ye hair of rush-like little rods, & under them hollow cases like to basins or little hives, in which is ye seed. It grows in rough & hilly places.

And here is what he tells us about *Euphorbia myrsinites,* which we photographed this time, complete with a spurge hawk-moth caterpillar, on the upper slopes of the highest mountain of Corfu:

but ye female which some have called Myrsinites, or Caryites, is like in nature to Daphnoeides & it hath leaves like to Myrsine [that is, garden myrtle], but greater, & strong, sharp, & prickly on ye top, but it sends out from ye root shoots a span long, and it bears a fruit every second year, like to ye nut, gently biting the tongue. This grows also in rough places.

These two descriptions ought really to suffice, but I cannot refrain from quoting you the third as

Euphorbia characias in Mistra

well, that of *Euphorbia cyparissias*, because this is the most succinct and vivid of the lot:

But Cyparissias doth send out a stalk a span long, or rather longer, somewhat red, out of which spring ye leaves like to those of ye Pine, yet tenderer and thinner; & it is wholly like to a pine new come up, whence also it is so-called. And this also is filled with white juice.

This is Dioscorides at his very best: and he keeps it up as he goes on to describe his last 4 'kinds of Tithymal', our photograph of one of which, *Euphorbia helioscopia*, was taken on or near the south-western coast of Ireland.

Now this, of course, is fine; with descriptions such as these there is a sporting chance of identifying a plant correctly. But unfortunately the chapter devoted to the seven kinds of τιθύμαλλος is not only just about the longest in the whole herbal, it is also just about the best. Far more often we get something like this, which is chapter 80 of Book III:

Elaphoboscum is a stalk like to Libanotis, or to Fennill, knotty, ye leaves of 2 fingers breadth, very long, as of Terebinth, broken about in a sharp manner, but the stalk hath very many little spriggs having tufts like unto Dill flowers, of a pale yellow, & ye seed like unto Dill. Ye root about ye length of three fingers ye thickness of a finger, white, sweet, edible; ye stalk being newly come up, is eaten as other herbs. They say that ye Hindes having fed on this very herb do hereby resist ye bitings of serpents, whence also ye seed is given with wine to ye serpent-bitten.

Well, if you happen to know what Libanotis, Fennill, Terebinth and Dill are, then you may flatter yourself that you have some mental picture, if

Euphorbia myrsinites

Tree spurge: Euphorbia sp. in North Africa

Euphorbia helioscopia

not a very precise one, of what Elaphoboscum looks like. But if that is what you are thinking, then, I ask, how can you be sure of what seems to me most improbable, that John Goodyer himself, the translator, correctly identified the ancient Greek plants which he so confidently renders as Fennill or Dill? And if your faith is still unshaken, then what are you going to do about the following, which comprises the whole of chapter 142 of Book II and is the only occasion throughout the whole herbal on which he mentions the plant in question:

Lampsana is a wild Olus, more nourishing and more agreeable to ye stomach than Lapathum, whose stalks and leaves are eaten being sod.*

I ask you!

I am afraid all this is a far cry from what you came to this meeting expecting. But if you care to invite me again, which after this evening is inconceivable, I will gladly conduct you on one of those tours, the staple diet of every branch of the Alpine Garden Society, through the Dolomites, the Swiss Alps, the Italian Alps, the French Alps, the Pyrenees – or even my garden.

---

* This, and other quotations on pp. 91, 93 and 94, are evidently taken from *The Greek Herbal of Dioscorides, illustrated by a Byzantine, A.D. 512; Englished by John Goodyer, A.D. 1655; edited and first printed, A.D. 1933, by Robert T. Gunther* (Oxford 1934) – Eds.

EPILOGUE

PETER WARREN

"What are you going to do about the following … ? 'Lampsana is a wild Olus, more nourishing and more agreeable to ye stomach than Lapathum, whose stalks and leaves are eaten being sod'. I ask you!" [See p. 96 above.]

Twenty-nine years after John Raven's Oxford lecture (*supra* pp. 79–96) and twenty-four years after the Gray Lectures, his work has itself become a stimulating part of the history of Greek botany. We may therefore glance at one or two post-Ravenian developments in his subject and begin to see his work in perspective, and we shall return to Lampsana and Lapathum. First we must acknowledge with admiration the combination of necessary but very different qualities he possessed and brought to bear on the difficult subject of the modern identification of ancient Greek plants and of ancient botanists' understanding of them: deep knowledge of and sensitivity to the ancient Greek language; thorough grounding in taxonomic botany, the Aegean flora (both real and depicted), landscape and ecology.

Since 1976 the task of identification has been greatly aided by a stream of outstanding botanical publications. Dr. Stearn refers to specialist studies in the introduction and the recent scientific bibliography is very large. Four of the five volumes of *Flora Europaea* had already appeared by 1976. Since then at a synthetic level we may note, in English alone and in order of appearance, A. Huxley and W. Taylor, *Flowers of Greece and the Aegean* (1977). O. Polunin, *Flowers of Greece and the Balkans. A Field Guide* (1980), B. Mathew, *The Crocus* (1982), A. Strid (ed.), *Mounain Flora of Greece*, I (1986), G. Sfikas, *Wild Flowers of Crete* (1987), the English edition of H. Baumann's *Die griechische Pflanzenwelt in Mythos, Kunst und Literatur* (1982), namely *Greek Wild Flowers and Plant Lore in Ancient Greece*, translated and augmented by W.T. Stearn and E.R. Stearn (1993), A. Strid and K. Tan (eds.), *Mountain Flora of Greece*, II (1991), and M. Blamey and C. Grey

Wilson, *Mediterranean Wild Flowers* (1993). These are scientific works, most written in the light of *Flora Europaea*, and they are superbly illustrated in colour. Another relevant and useful book, again with beautiful photographs, is A. Dodds Niebuhr, *Herbs of Greece*, already published in 1970. We now have, for Crete, Kasos and Karpathos, the *sine qua non, Flora of the Cretan Area. Annotated Checklist & Atlas* by N.J. Turland, L. Chilton and J.R. Press (1993) and *Flora of Crete. A Supplement* by L. Chilton and N.J. Turland (1997), themselves built upon Sir Colville Barclay's meticulous *Crete. Checklist of the vascular plants* (*Englera* 6) (1986). Plants naturally flourish in O. Rackham and J. Moody, *The Making of the Cretan Landscape* (1996).

Iconographic evidence for plants is richly evident from the Minoan and Cycladic civilization of the Bronze Age Aegean. That found by S. Marinatos in the paintings from Akrotiri on Thera, circa 1520 B.C., was excellently discussed by Lyvia Morgan in her book, *The Miniature Wall Paintings of Thera* (1988), pp. 17–32. Meanwhile the material itself is brilliantly illustrated in C. Doumas, *The Wall-Paintings of Thera* (1992). New evidence from excavations directed by the writer at Knossos is discussed in 'The fresco of the garlands from Knossos' (in P. Darcque and J.-C. Poursat (eds.), *L'iconographie minoenne* (1985)) and on the squill, *Drimia maritima*, in *Aux origines de l'hellénisme, La Créte et la Gréce* (1985).

While John Raven made questions of plant identification the central theme of his lectures – and so he would surely have delighted in the information, illustration, new discoveries and discussion in the works cited – he touched on many other aspects. How do they fare? Among structuralists, post-structuralists, deconstructionists, post-deconstructionists floral texts are likely to be seen as literary *topoi*, embedded in the rest of their texts and not open to real-world (archaeological or botanical) topographical identification. A flowering meadow constitutes or symbolizes a stage of sexual change in Greek poetic texts from the *Homeric Hymn to Demeter* to Moschus. Plants are also used to make symbolic statements about the social world, a theme well developed by Richard Buxton in *Imaginary Greece. The contexts of mythology* (1994), and more widely, by Jack Goody in *The Culture of Flowers* (1993). But none of this negates botanical topography. The pool of Hylas is plausibly linked to Theocritus' real world (on Kos, whether or not to a precise spot) as well as to his poetical imagination.

Another aspect, rather briefly alluded to by Raven ('mere oral tradition', Gray Lecture 2), is the popular use of a very extensive range of wild plants for many purposes – food, medicine, health generally, perfumes, aromatics, dye-stuffs, decoration, and religious and secular symbolism. This tradition has assuredly been continuous in Crete from the Minoan Bronze Age until today, as doubtless generally in the Greek world. Its relevance and importance for the present subject lie in the accompanying popular nomenclature and identification of the plants used. Raven, like others, recognized that the same names are not infrequently used by rural Greeks today as by Theophrastus, Theocritus, Krateuas, Celsus, Dioscorides, Pliny, Galen, Oreibasios and Hesychius in antiquity. Renaissance botanists, in particular Luigi Anguillara, Pierre Belon, Onorio Belli, Prospero Alpini and, later, John Ray, recorded these popular names alongside the names they attributed by their linking of plants observed in the field to the descriptions and illustrations of Dioscorides and others. There are many problems in the history of plant nomenclature, but the oral tradition is continuous and must itself have supplied Dioscorides, his predecessors and successors with names of plants which were in continuous use. John Raven's delightful quotation of Sir

Arthur Hill's meeting in 1934 with a botanist monk on Mount Athos armed with a manuscript copy of Dioscorides is almost anticipated by Simon Corda of Genoa plant-hunting with an old Cretan peasant lady, expert in plants and Dioscoridean names, in the thirteenth century! As for the Lampsana and Lapathum of Dioscorides (*supra*), it is pleasing to note that what is first documented in Epicharmus, fifth century B.C. (λαψάνη, *Sinapis arvensis*) could be recorded by me at Kalyves, Crete, on 18 August 1991, while Lapathum (λάπαθον, *Rumex* spp.), first known in a third century B.C. papyrus, is still gathered, likewise for food, everywhere in the island today.

On the medicinal use of plants and the huge influence of Dioscorides, Raven moved to a much more positive view in the Gray Lectures from that given to the Alpine Garden Society in Oxford five years earlier. John Riddle's brilliant and persuasively argued book, *Dioscorides on Pharmacy and Medicine*, was published in 1985. Raven had argued that Dioscorides, like Pliny, came nearer to anticipating the Linnaean binomial system than Theophrastus ever did and that although he did not construct an overall botanical classificatory system, his individual chapters have a clear and consistent internal sequence and structure. Riddle goes much further and advances the thesis, at length and with conviction, that Dioscorides did have an organizing principle, based not on a botanical classificatory system but on the medical or drug properties (affinities) of plants, with groupings according to the similarities of their properties; the groupings were lost by the later alphabetization of Dioscorides' plants. The properties, Riddle argues, are sometimes close to the modern pharmacological order of perception of the behaviour of drugs made from natural products. Riddle's and other specialist studies, as well as the much wider contemporary acceptance of the value of aromatherapy (cf. Jean Valnet, *The Practice of Aromatherapy* (1982) [French edition *Aromathérapie* (1980), much reprinted]), are reinstating the anciently perceived value of plants in medicine.

Epilogue

We return, lastly, to John Raven's central subject, identifications, since here too matters have not stood still. In his second Gray Lecture he describes three endemic species of tulips in Crete (*T. bakeri, T. cretica* and *T. saxatilis*). He established their altitudinal ranges and habitats. The genus is currently held to have two Cretan endemics, *T. cretica* and *T. doefleri*, as well as two non-endemics, *T. goulimyi* and *T. saxatilis* (whose range is wider than Crete). *T. bakeri* is included in the synonymy of *T. saxatilis*. See Turland, Chilton and Press (*supra*), p. 186, who note that *T. bakeri* is treated as a separate species by others. Difficulties or impossibilities of distinguishing between Minoan and Theran representations of tulips, crocuses and *Gagea* spp. are referred to by Dr. Stearn in the Introduction. Raven rightly cites pictures of crocuses gathered for saffron. Whether this is *C. sativus* or the wild form *C. cartwrightianus* or the similar Cretan endemic *C. oreocreticus*, is currently under discussion. There are clear depictions with prominent red style branches from the writer's recent excavations at Knossos. Finally, the magnificent frieze of huge plants painted in the House of the Ladies at Thera. John Raven followed Marinatos's interpretation as *Pancratium maritimum*, the sand lily. The writer endeavoured to show that the plants are papyrus, one of the finest of the many renderings of that plant in Minoan and Theran painting, a plant of fertility and regeneration for the Egyptians and likewise sacred for the Minoans, in whose island it very probably grew. It is churlish to end an epilogue with point-scoring. But I have no doubt John Raven would have relished the discussion. We certainly need his spirit and continuing influence in the labyrinth of ancient Greek botany and the subsequent history of the nomenclature, identification and uses of the Aegean's paradise of beautiful plants.

Notes on Contributors

Nicholas Jardine is Professor of History and Philosophy of the Sciences at the University of Cambridge. His books include *The Birth of History and Philosophy of Science: Kepler's 'A Defense of Tycho against Ursus' with Essays on its Provenance and Significance* (1984), *The Fortunes of Enquiry* (1986), *Romanticism and the Sciences*, ed. with Andrew Cunningham (1990), and *The Scenes of Enquiry: On the Reality of Questions in the Sciences* (1991). He is editor of *Studies in History and Philosophy of Science*. His current research projects are on historical consciousness in the sciences and, in collaboration with Alain Segonds, on priority disputes in early modern cosmology.

Alice Lindsell took the Classical Tripos from Newnham, Cambridge in 1903 and 1904, followed by an MA from Trinity College, Dublin. She returned to Newnham to be secretary to the Principal 1913–15.

In the First World War she became an organiser of the Land Army for the Board of Agriculture and here, to quote from Stearn in *Annales Musei Goulandris*, 9 (1994), "A one-time Newnham College student, A.G. Briselden, who worked under Miss Lindsell in the Women's Land Army, wrote an amusing parody of Lewis Carroll 'The Walrus and the Carpenter' with Miss Lindsell and a mournful local country woman at West Walton as its characters, of which the following is an extract:

> Miss Lindsell and the Mournful One
> Discourse of doleful deeds.
> They wept like anything to see
> Such quantities of weeds.
> 'It's very obvious', they said,
> 'It's hoeing that it needs.
>
> If seven maids with seven hoes
> Hoed it for half a year,
> Do you suppose,' Miss Lindsell said.
> That they could get it clear?
> 'I doubt it', said the Mournful One.
> And shed a bitter tear.
>
> Miss Lindsell and the Mournful One
> Worked on an hour or so,
> And then they rested on a stack
> Conveniently low.
> And all the little workers stood
> And waited in a row.
>
> 'The time has come', Miss Lindsell said.
> 'To eat of many things:
> Of paste and marg and sausages
> And taters grown at Wings
> And we'll discuss how windfalls fall
> and whether wasps have stings'.
>
> 'I weep for you', Miss Lindsell said.
> 'I deeply sympathize'.
> With sobs and tears she sorted out
> The onions of largest size,
> Holding her pocket handkerchief
> Before her streaming eyes."

Alice Lindsell's main career, however, was for twenty years as Warden of the hostel for Bedford College, London. We presume that the University year left her time for her study of Greek botany and the beautiful water-colour portraits she painted. See also pp. 43 and 57 above.

Anna Raven is an artist and garden designer, studied at the Bath Academy of Art, 1976–79 and has exhibited twice in London at the Rebecca Hosack Gallery.

Faith Raven is an environmentalist, landowner, social worker, gardener and photographer.

William Thomas Stearn, C.B.E., born in 1911 in Cambridge and educated there, was from 1933 to 1952 (apart from war-service in England, India and Burma) librarian of the Royal Horticultural Society's Lindley Library, from 1952 to 1976 botanist in the British Museum (Natural History) and from 1977 to 1983 visiting professor in the Department of Botany and Agricultural Botany, University of Reading. From 1976 onwards he has edited the Greek multilingual biological periodical *Annales Musei Goulandris* (Kifissia, Athens). He is the author of *Botanical Latin, Flower Artists of Kew, Stearn's Dictionary of Plant Names for Gardeners*

etc., numerous contributions to learned journals and part-author (with W. Blunt) of *The Art of Botanical Illustration*, and (with P.H. Davis) *Peonies of Greece* etc.

Peter Warren is Professor of Ancient History and Classical Archaeology and formerly Pro-Vice-Chancellor at the University of Bristol. His major research field is Aegean archaeology, especially the Minoan civilization of Crete and its international connexions. He has directed excavations in Crete at Myrtos, Debla and for many years at Knossos and has written *Minoan Stone Vases* (1969), *Myrtos, an Early Bronze Age Settlement in Crete* (1972), *The Aegean Civilizations* (1975. 2nd ed. 1989), *Minoan Religion as Ritual Action* (1988) and, with V. Hankey, *Aegean Bronze Age Chronology* (1989). Other research interests are early travellers in Greece and the Aegean and the history of botany and the use of plants in Crete, some of which he tries to grow in Gloucestershire.

BOTANICAL INDEX